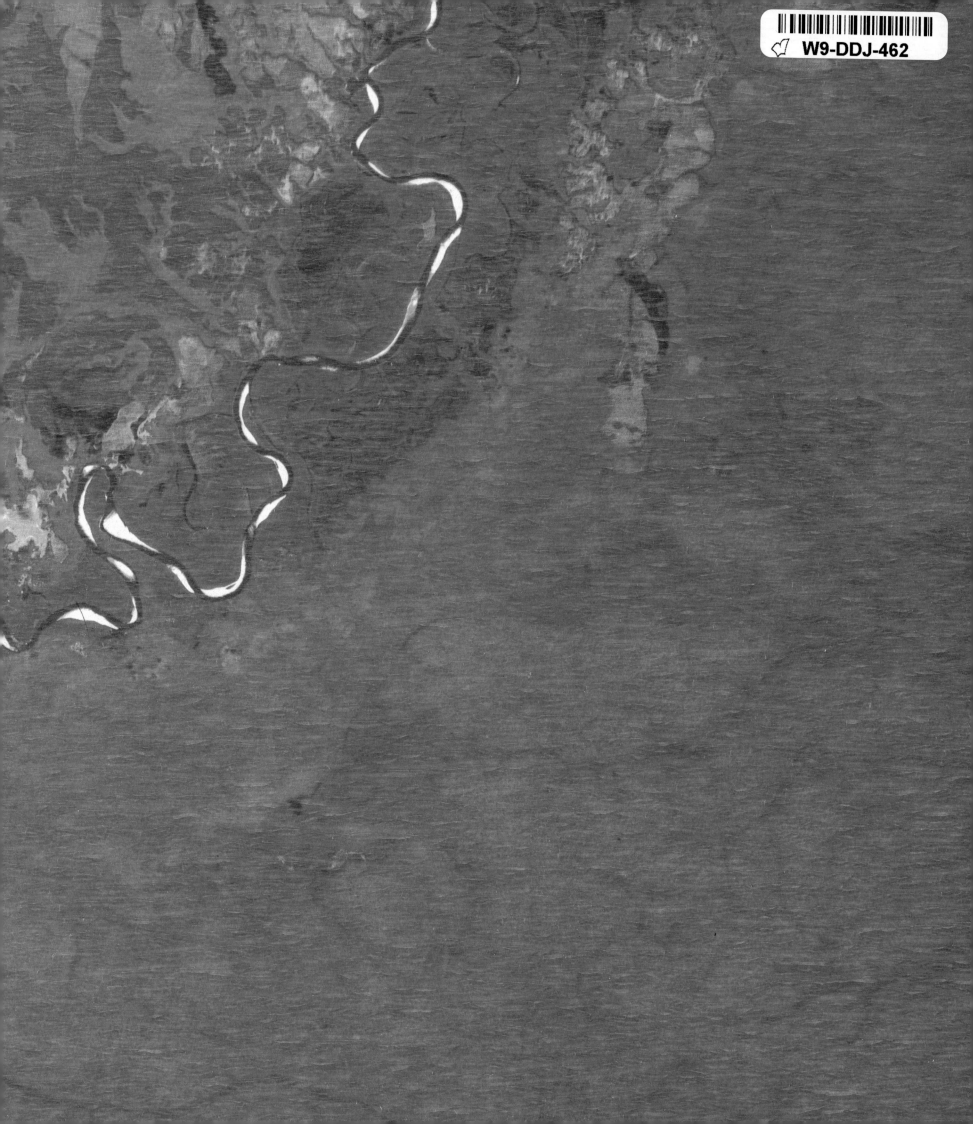

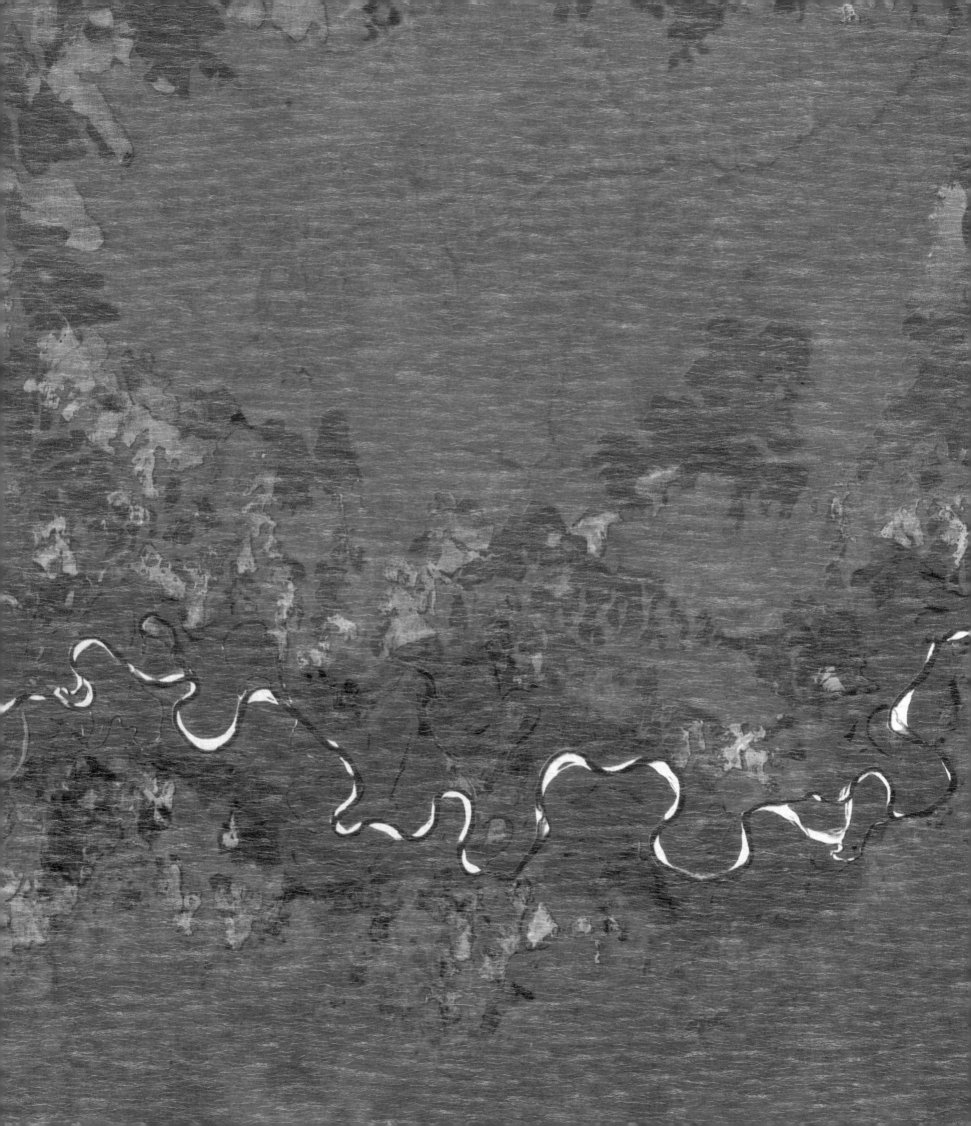

The Andean Countries

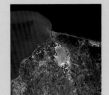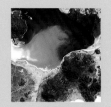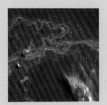

BY SATELLITE

ANIVERSARIO

25

CAF
Corporación Andina de Fomento

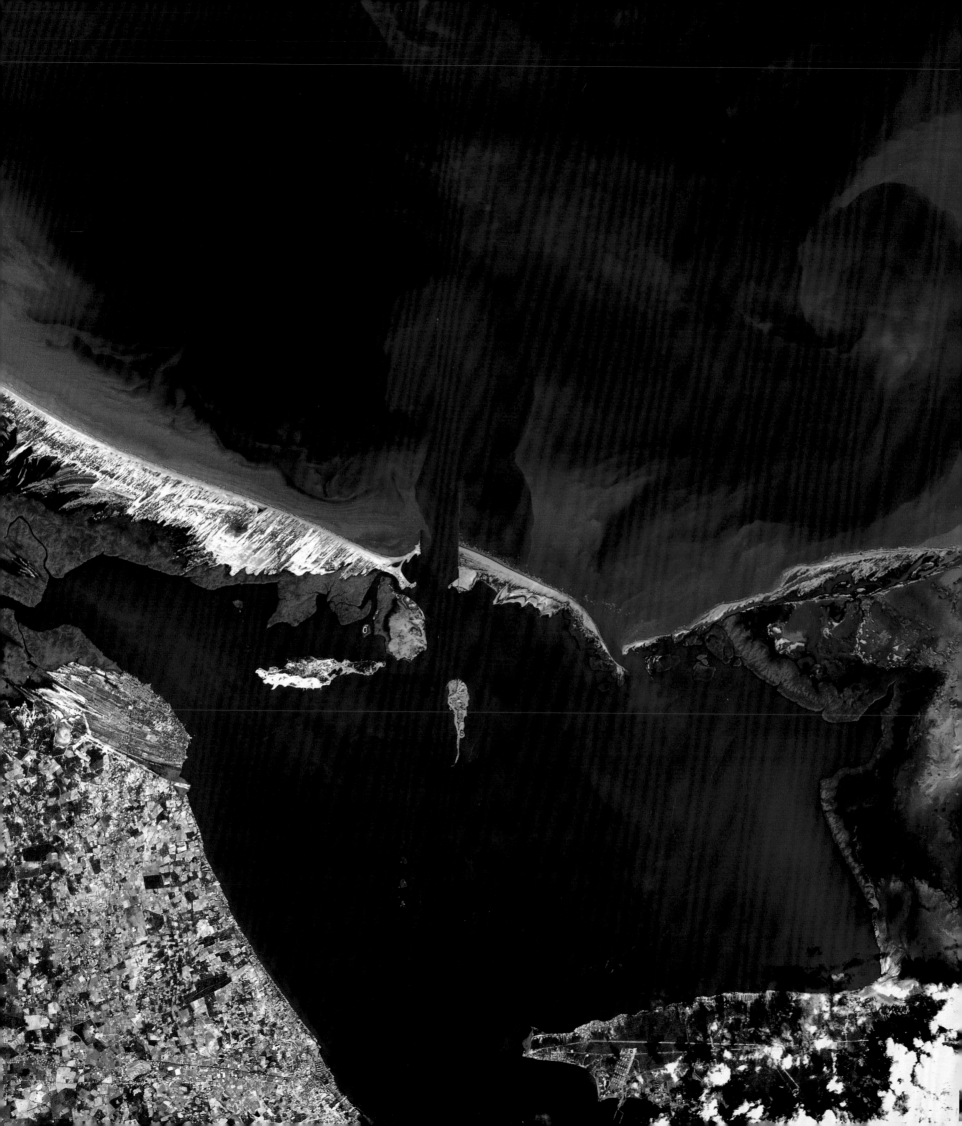

The Andean Countries

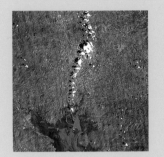

BY SATELLITE

Direction, design and edition
BENJAMIN VILLEGAS

Texts
L. ENRIQUE GARCIA
GUSTAVO WILCHES-CHAUX
OLIVIER BERNARD

Villegas editores

Layout
MERCEDES CEDEÑO

Digital cartography
GERCON Ltda.

English version
ANDREW ALEXANDER REID

© Publishing Rights
VILLEGAS EDITORES 1995
Avenida 82 No.11-50, Interior 3
Tel 616-1788. Fax 616-0020
Santafé de Bogotá, D.C., Colombia

© Rights on Images
CNES French Space Agency

First edition
April 1995

ISBN 958-9393-02-0

Printed in Japan by
TOPPAN PRINTING COMPANY

The publisher wishes to express special thanks to
Corporación Andina de Fomento (CAF)
and its president
L. ENRIQUE GARCIA
for the patronage and support granted to this work
without which its publication would have been impossible.

The publisher also wishes to thank
SPOT IMAGE
for its faith in the project
and for providing its
most beautiful pictures
of the Andean countries
and neighbouring areas.

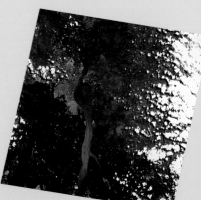

Page 4 photo caption:
Ven/25. *Bahía del Tablazo and mouth of Lake Maracaibo in the Gulf
of Venezuela. State of Zulia*. Page 67.

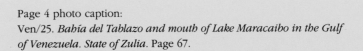

Contents

A World without Frontiers

he human eye's relationship with the surrounding environment is vast, complex and intriguing. For those who have, quite literally, plunged into a cave like Altamira and, lying on the ground, witnessed in front of their eyes the slow emergence from shadows of reddish outlines which gradually take the shape of a doe or a bison, the initial miracle, which exalts the human condition, repeats itself with the same wonder. They behold the first representation of what the human eye beholds.

Magical spell and memory, under this mantle of darkness one of the greatest breakthroughs of the mind has been preserved, by conquering matter and putting it to use. Moulding themselves on the cave's crevices and bends and transcending them in one fell swoop, by a pure act of creation: the doe flees, the bison stampedes again, stalked by hunters. A record of what was has thus remained, kept intact to our day by the propitious milieu of this inner sanctuary. The crypt is now a temple where man has defeated nature and preserved his works.

But the eye, in this symbolic cavern, didn't embrace everything. It had to go back up to the surface, discover, like the Italian primitives, trees and rocks… Exalt the human figure in imperishable fashion, like Leonardo, like Dürer, on lofty cupolas deep below the ground. The discovery of perspective meant situating man, minute indeed in front of the might of nature, like a mere footnote to the scenery, but already converted into a measure of all things. Small wonder, then, that upon reaching the beaches of America, such images placed themselves in the foreground. They interposed themselves between ourselves and a nature which, at the time,

Small town of Villazón in the semi-arid southern stretches of
the Bolivian altiplano, on the border with Argentina.

Bol/166, page 202

was considered aggressive and voracious, or at best more bewildering and extreme than in Europe… A nature bursting at the seams. Furthermore, one must keep in mind that, before the 16th century, no accurate map of the world existed, as Colombian essayist Germán Arciniegas pointed out in *La Imagen Cambiante de los Mapas*.

It was at that time when arose the idea of putting the entire world on a patch of leather. To paint the world on a sheepskin proved another of man's impossible attempts to grasp a reality which eluded him on all the points of the compass rose. Nonetheless, thanks to this initiative, America became a name known to all, after featuring for the first time on one of these maps, which, seen today, seem more like erratic fantasies straight out of the magical realism school.

But nonetheless, and as years passed by, Latin American countries acquired self-awareness, and gained knowledge of their territory, through certain images where we identified. Such was one of Bolívar's achievements, in the impetuous onslaught of his cavalcade of liberation, leaving us five countries in his wake and striving in his feverish dream towards the ideal of a Greater Nation, which would ultimately have stretched from the Rio Grande to Patagonia. Or, on a minor scale but in a peaceful manner, one of the accomplishments of Agustín Codazzi, an Italian who happened to be Colombian, or Venezuelan, to boot, and who contributed during the last century to a more accurate cartography of our lands.

Still, this proved wanting. Only when we managed to soar up to the skies and look down on Earth from an altitude of 830 km., through 200 satellite photographs deciphered by computer, did we begin to truly apprehend who we are, and what planet we inhabit.

As always happens, the first impression is totally mind-boggling: we belong to an abstract painting. A few intense strokes, hard to define. Some vivid smudges which little by little become intelligible: red for jungle, white for clouds, blue for sea, non-polluted at best. Jagged mountains, as rough as the hide of a prehistoric animal, in the same way the Andes strike us seen through the window of an airplane, with the Biblical abruptness that Neruda sang in his haunting poems… And tiny rivers, glimpsed from such heights as delicate, zigzag threads, as random touches of light in the midst of the dense tree mass.

The first certainty to strike us: there are no frontiers. Lands flow into each other; what we thought isolated is in fact interrelated. We find a tightly-woven physical cohesion which ranges from the lost spring half-buried in the jungle to the water tap opened in Caracas, Lima, La Paz, Santa Fe de Bogotá, Asuncíon or Buenos Aires. Everything is part of a whole, without which we couldn't

Cabo Manglares and estuary of a branch of the Mira river on
the Colombian Pacific coast, near the border with Ecuador.

Col/70, page 123

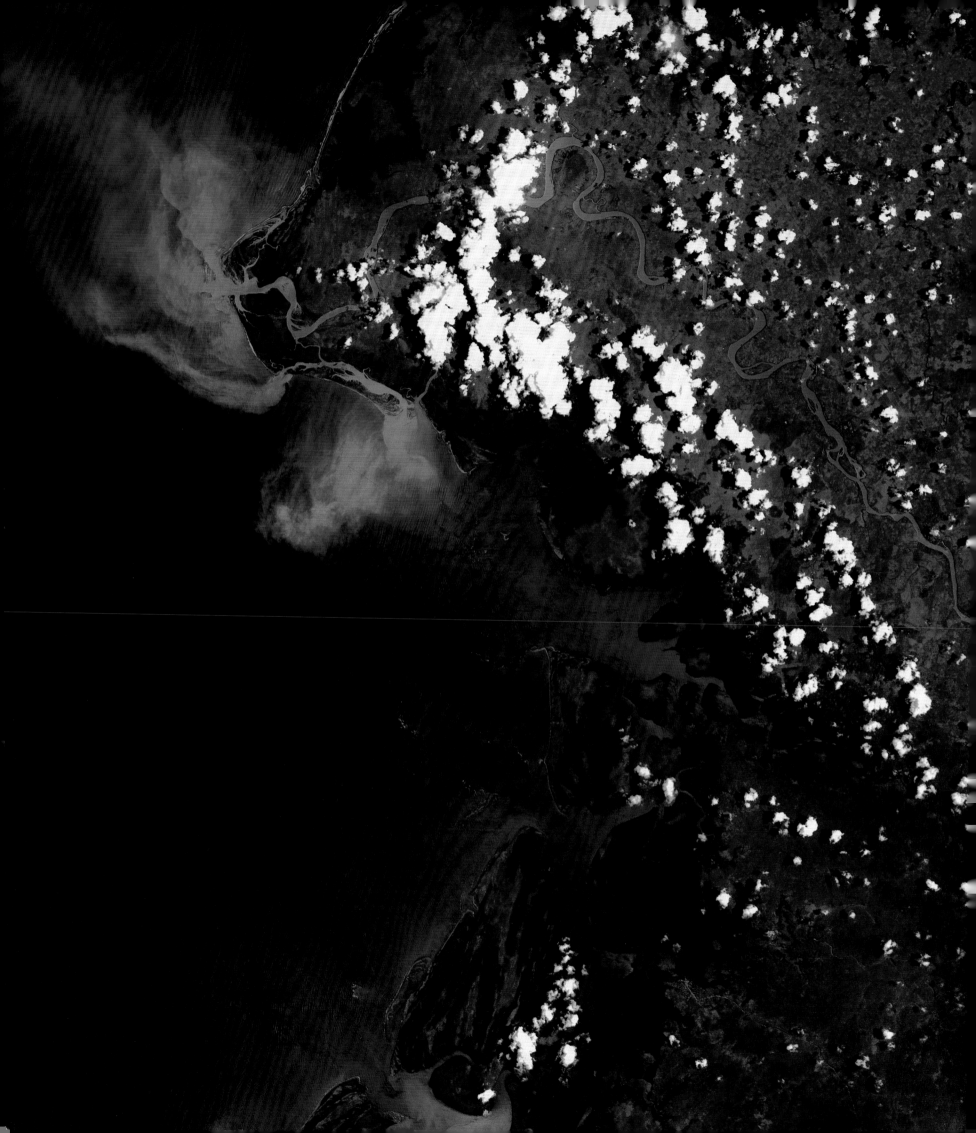

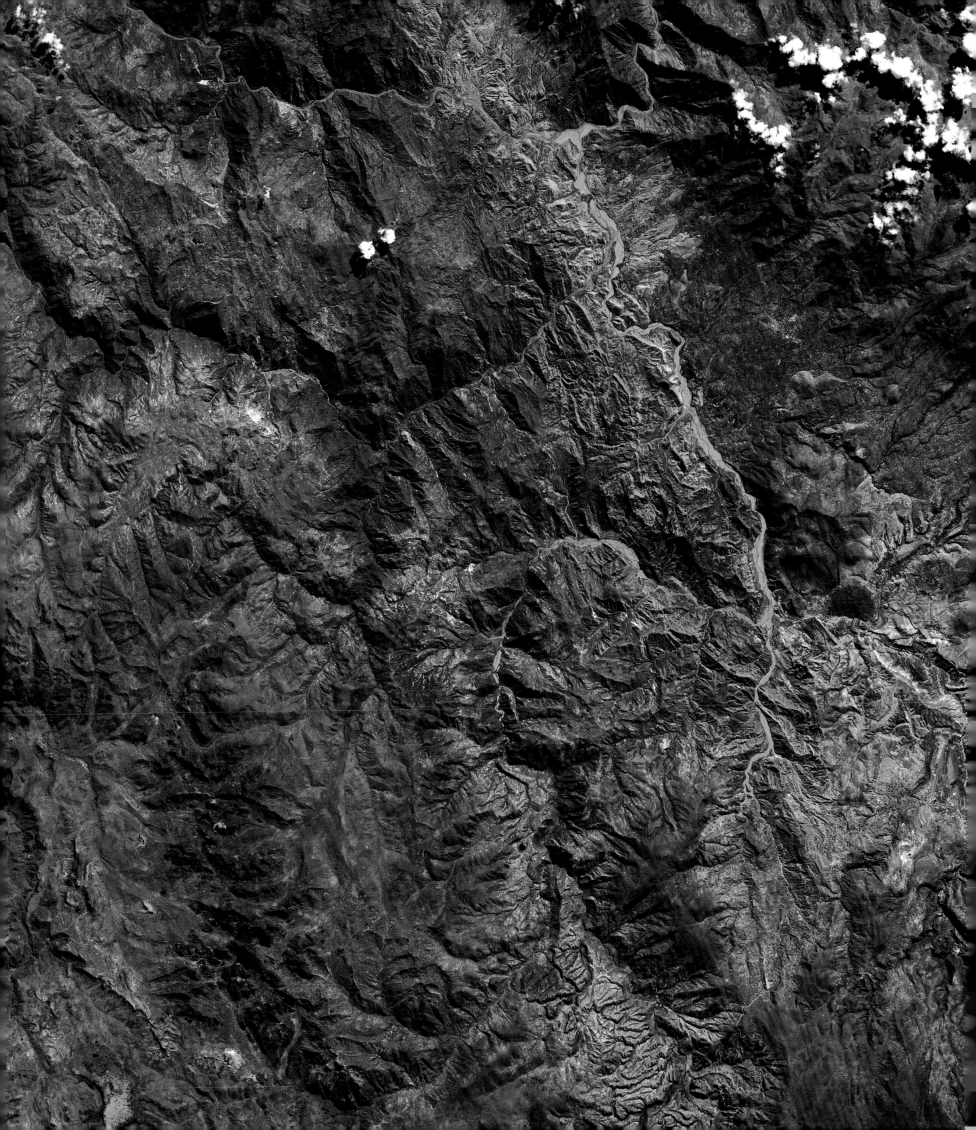

live. Thus, from river basins to desert zones, from oceans renewed by unending ebb and flow to estuaries of rivers rotting with refuse, we begin to apprehend a different story. A tangible story, at ground level, observed with enough perspective to grasp in its unequaled wholeness. Here the Earth's surface reveals to us its eruptions and telluric movements; and the jungle the presence of new groups of settlers who decided to fell trees to plant corn, just like our most remote ancestors, 40,000 years B.C.

Each of these photographs encompasses a comparatively small area of 60 by 60 kilometres, but the lesson they ultimately provide us is to think big. Within a whole where we are all dependent of each other, and the slightest movement reverberates and undulates throughout this electronic screen flickering with alarm signals –a threat of erosion there!– as if in joy of recognition: truly, and thanks to these pictures, we all feel at the same time minute but essential. This part of the world is our home and we must take care of it. Seen from above, men also form a constellation. The *Corporación Andina de Fomento* has always felt part of the American constellation, throughout its first 25 years of existence.

To offer new and original prospects for an age-old ambition such as integration, represents a challenge for us, in the financial sphere, who outline a collective project which transcends us, and that we cannot elude in its immediate and concrete responsibility.

To all of us, in all the American countries, the amazing and novel pictures in this book open up an unsuspected dimension. The American eye opens on its own habitat in a futuristic projection beyond our wildest imagination. But the future, in all certainty, is now. The future that we must all build, from the updated consciousness that these pages unfurl to us of human and natural wealth, and of the unique beauty of these countries that we proudly admire and for which we toil without respite. Seen from the satellite in flight, the Earth becomes pleasant and hospitable. This Earth is ours. Let us preserve it.

L. ENRIQUE GARCIA

CEO of CAF

Outskirts of the city of Ayacucho
in the Peruvian Andes.

Per/112, page 163

The Eye of God

A man from the village of Neguá, on the coast of Colombia, managed to soar high up in the skies. On his return, he told
his story. He said that he had contemplated human life from above. And he said that we are a sea of little flames.
"The world is so", he revealed. "A mass of people, a sea of little flames"
Each person shines with his own light among all the others. There are not two flames alike. There are big flames and small
flames and flames of all colours. There are people with a serene flame, oblivious even of the wind, and people with a wild
flame, which fills the air with sparks. Some flames, foolish flames, neither shed light nor burn; but others blaze with such
ardent life that one cannot look at them without blinking, and whoever comes near catches fire.
EDUARDO GALEANO, El Libro de los Abrazos

All that's essential attains unity.
Once unity is attained the sky clears up.
Once unity is attained the earth becomes secure.
Once unity is attained the spirit becomes powerful.
Once unity is attained the valley finds its plenitude.
TAO TE KING

hat would the inhabitant of another galaxy, venturing through the hazardous stretches of the Solar System,

think of Earth? Before reaching our neighbourhood, he would surely have had to pass by Pluto and its satellite

Charon (almost the size of the mother planet), and by icy Neptune, covered by a mist between greenish and

blue, like the wings of butterflies in the Colombian emerald region. He would have photographed, (or recorded

in some manner or other) the turbulences and swirls of the atmosphere of Uranus, of the same colour as our clouds and our seas.

He would have taken advantage of the strong pull exerted by the gigantic presence of Saturn to station himself in Jupiter's orbit,

Ciudad Guayana in the state of Delta Amacuro,
near the estuary of the Orinoco.

Ven/6, page 61

and would have been forced to use full propulsion not to be dragged down by its gravity. He would have explored the Big Red Spot and the complex realm of storms and hurricanes which engulf the equatorial region of the largest planet in the Solar System. He would have then slipped through the millions of asteroids which revolve in an orbit closer to the Sun, and would have skirted Mars, the rocky planet known to Earthmen under the name of the god of war, and Phobos and Deimos, its two sinister and dark moons bearing the epithets of hatred and terror.

And then, all of a sudden, in the midst of the iridescent twilight of the velvet of interstellar space, he would have stumbled upon a planet, the surface conformation of which would have made his sensors quiver wildly on detecting the existence of an element absent in other planets of the Solar System: the space traveller would have found a bubble of water at 150 million km. from the Sun. For him (or her, or him/her), the presence of water could well have failed to mean anything special, except perhaps the discovery of a new molecule to jot down in his notebook on the universe.

Or maybe something would have clicked. Maybe Earth would have enthralled him (or her). Maybe (we don't know to what type of signals, particles or radiations his sensors would be tuned to), he would manage to sense or perceive that, intimately linked to the presence of water, a phenomenon exists on the planet of which he (or she, or he/she), the space traveller, is another manifestation. Maybe it would have dawned on the wanderer that Life exists on Earth. That Earth is a living planet. He would have spotted the "little flames" that the man from the village of Neguá saw, in Galeano's tale.

He would have "caught fire"… And that would have forced him to stay on and explore. To try and understand. To experience.

He would have circumnavigated the Earth and found white and bluish ripples and spirals, like in the atmosphere of Uranus, hurricanes like on Jupiter, icecaps like on Pluto (but composed with water), orange-coloured storms like on Mars, whirls and spirals reminding him of faraway galaxies, undulating formations that he would later find again, after meeting Earthmen, on another scale, sometimes in microscopic dimensions, in the carnal envelope of humans, in the surface of leaves, in the lichen clinging to stones, in the bark of trees. Ramified configurations which –he would later discover– are the deltas of rivers, the hydrographic basins, the arborescent configuration of cordilleras and mountains… and that he would also find in the neurones of living beings, in their circulatory systems, pulmonary structures, in the roots of plants… And time and again, in the midst of random formations, of the erratic itinerary of watercourses, of the turmoil of clouds, of the capricious and foaming evanescence of coastal regions: unexpectedly,

Galapagos islands in the Colon archipelago, which belongs to
Ecuador, over a thousand kilometres away.
———
Ecu/71, page 124

16

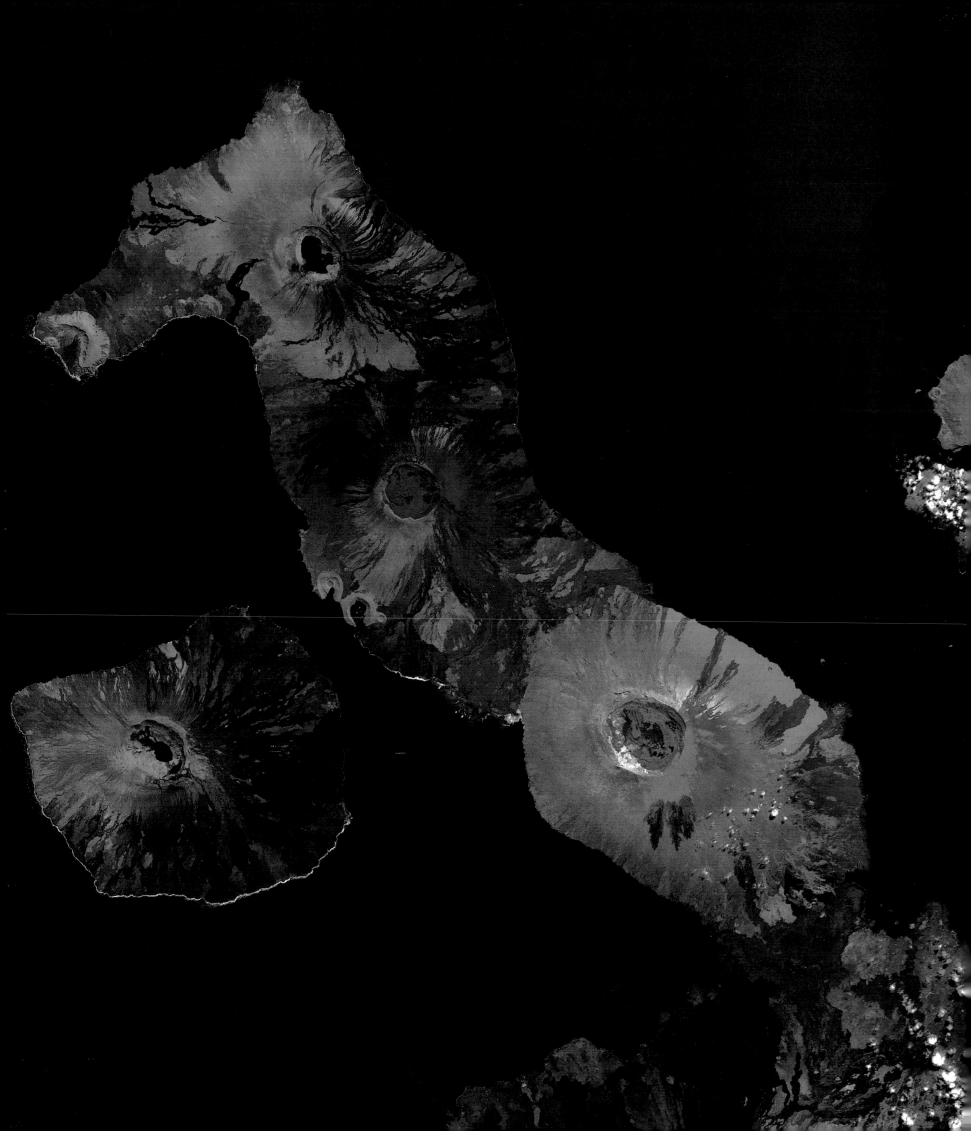

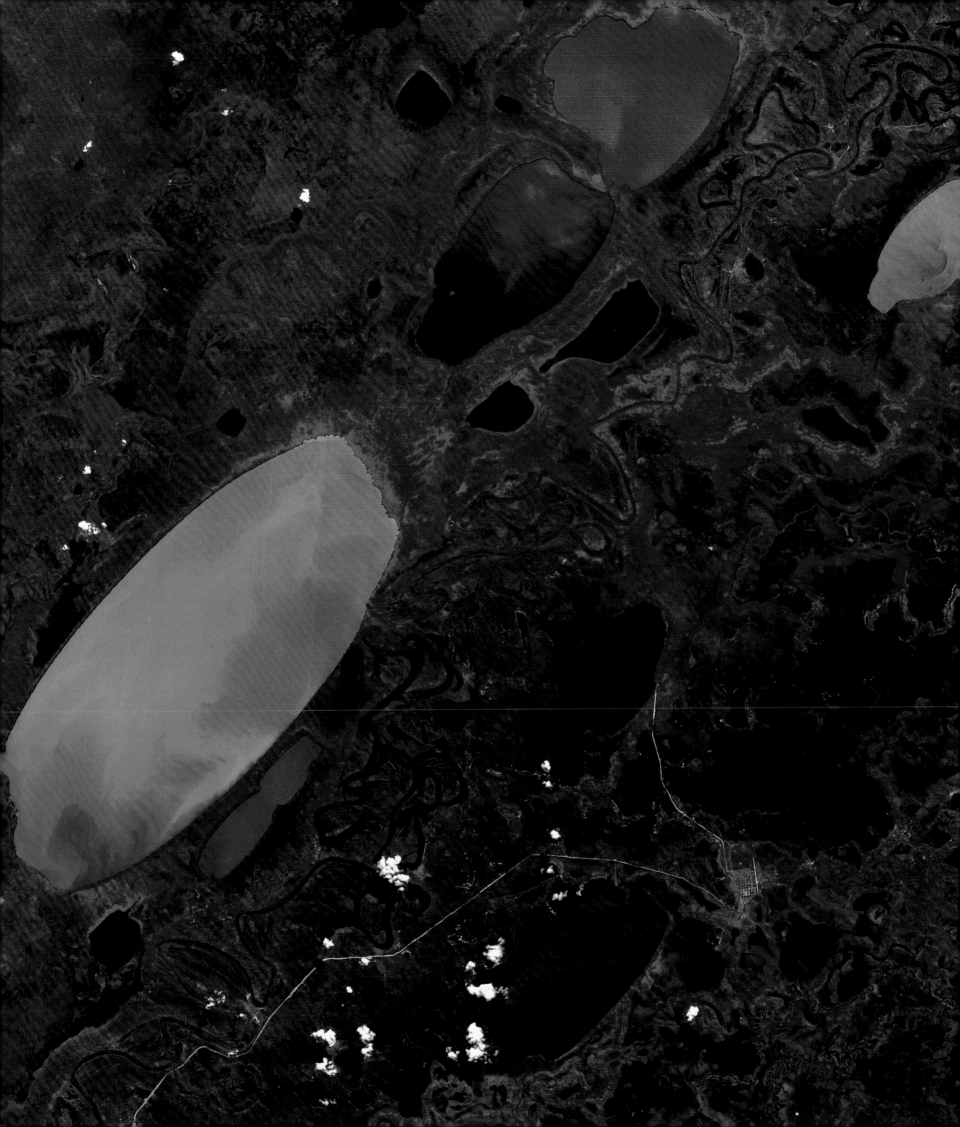

straight lines, perfect circles, rectangles, criss-cross patterns, squares, farmlands, dams, bridges, roads… human presence. For some reason (possibly the intensity of the "little flames" that the man from Neguá saw), the space traveller would place his vessel in orbit over the expanse of mainland that Earthmen know as America, and, to be precise, over the rough cone shape that we call South America.

The space traveller would be unaware –and if one told him he probably wouldn't understand– that on this cone called South America exist 12 "independent countries" and two "colonial possessions", concepts that would mean nothing to his electromagnetic vibration sensors, only receptive to formations, turbulences and the rhythm of mountains and seas.

We, Earthmen, could see the Earth from afar, with our own eyes, for the first time, from an Apollo spacecraft, in December 1968. We began this endeavour in earnest only ten years earlier, when the Russians launched their first satellite into space, Sputnik-1, which weighed a little under 84 kg. and was 58 cm. in diameter. The possibility to see the "full Earth", to see ourselves from outer space, writes Fritjof Capra, constitutes the crowning achievement of space exploration.

Our leap into space –which turned us into *de facto* extraterrestrials– is justified by the better knowledge we attain of ourselves.

"Who has gone away from home has already returned", says Borges in his poem-prologue to the I Ching.

II

In his book *Manual del Pesimista,* Eric Marcus relates that his grandmother Ethel Sand was born at the end of the 19th century in Lvov, Austria, grew up in Poland, and in the late twenties emigrated from the Soviet Union. "The funny thing is", writes Marcus, "that before boarding the boat to Brooklyn, grandma had never left the village where she was born. It was not grandma but territorial limits which moved!".

National borders, that someone dubbed "the scars of history", are invisible from space.

The orbiting space traveller, who decides to visit South America, will be unable to know, on board his ship, which country is the biggest, which is the most inhabited, where Chile begins and Argentina ends, where the border passes between Colombia and Venezuela or between Peru and Ecuador…

Cluster of small lakes originating from the rivers and swamps
close to north-eastern Bolivia's tropical rain forest.

Bol/151, page 198

19

But indeed he will see –or his detectors of chlorophyll, living beings and water will tell him– that in South America there are almost six million square kilometres (5,897,795 to be exact) of the most luxuriant jungles, with the greatest variety of species, on the planet. His sensors will register trees absorbing carbonic gas from the air to keep the Earth's climate stable. They will inform him that, of all the rivers surveyed on the globe, the largest flows from one end to the other of this jungle, that Earthmen call Amazonia, and that this river, the Amazon, along its 6,500 km. length, gathers the waters of a basin covering almost seven million square kilometres (6,869,344 to be exact). Or a million more if one throws in the Orinoco.

The space traveller will find on the western edge of South America, like a cyclopean wall over the Pacific, the Andean Cordillera, the planet's largest mountain range, 8,900 km. long. He will see it tower with the Aconcagua to an altitude of almost seven kilometres (6,959 m.), to then tumble down to the coasts of the Caribbean like a river delta and stretch a gigantic arm to the seashores of Venezuela. If he is versed in geology and techtonics, he will understand that the cordillera surges upwards under the tremendous pressure exerted by the South American plate (over which the continent "sails" on magma) on the Pacific plate (upon which lies the ocean bed). The spaceship's instruments will detect active volcanoes all along the cordillera (among which the Cotopaxi, the planet's highest active volcano, 5,897 m. above sea level), geological faults, accumulated tensions and brutal fractures, which periodically disrupt the lives of people of the Andes.

High up in the cordillera, at 3,835 m. above sea level, he will discover an eerie but splendid lake spreading over 8,300 km.2. If he has managed to get his hands on a world atlas, he will learn that is called Titicaca, and that it lies between Bolivia and Peru. Towards the south-west, he will behold the 180,000 km.2 of the Atacama desert, perhaps the most barren in the world.

Then, to the north, a territory inhabited by humans for at least 20,000 years: present-day Peru, from where the Incas expanded their empire. And if he follows the coastline, from the border, indicated on the atlas, between Ecuador and Colombia up to Panama, he will find, in this continental armpit of sorts, a narrow strip of jungle that biologists call the Biogeographic Chocó, one of the rainiest, zaniest and species-abundant corners of the Earth.

On the other side, in the north-eastern part of the base of the South American cone, the Guyanas Massif (or Plateau) appears, a fragment of the ancient shield which crumples the terrestrial crust, and presses the Andean Cordillera ever upwards. North of Amazonia, if the space traveller has a way of looking through the clouds, he will be able to see, in the middle of the jungle, the

Salar del Hombre Muerto along the Sierra de Aguas Calientes.
Province of Salta, Argentina.

Arg/186, page 208

outcrop of *Tepuyes* (which means mountain in the Pemón Indian tongue), gravelly plateaus carved by the unrelenting erosion of 500 million years. And from one of them –the *Tepui* of Auyan– he will listen in awe to water crashing down an abyss almost a thousand metres deep: Angel Falls, the Earth's highest waterfall.

Then, to the north-east, he will contemplate the Brazilian Central Massif, and to the south, the Amazon plains: the bed of an ancient sea which formed when the Andes began to soar and which "drained" in the late Tertiary period through the mighty Orinoco and Amazon.

And further still, stretch the desolate wastelands of north-eastern Brazil, which contrast with the humid, green lushness of the Amazon jungle. Further again, in Paraguay, the inhospitable Gran Chaco unfurls its bleak wilderness. Where the atlas shows this country's frontier with Brazil, on the Paraná river (South America's second longest), lies the highest-capacity hydroelectric plant on the planet: Itaipú (which, together with the Yacyretá dam, will make Paraguay the world's biggest exporter of hydroelectric energy).

Not far away, in the Iguazú, along a distance of four kilometres, roar 60 metre-high cataracts on the limits between Argentina and Brazil. (The Guairá Falls were silenced and flooded by the waters of the Itaipú dam.)

Then an amazingly fertile land of plenty, reminiscent of Mesopotamia, shared by Brazil, Argentina and Uruguay, spreads out to the River Plate, on the Atlantic Ocean.

And the Pampas and Patagonia, the Magellan Straits, Tierra del Fuego and Cape Horn, the southernmost tip of the continent, last stop before the Antarctic.

From there, on the Pacific, looking again to the north, tens of thousands of islands seem to agglutinate before forming continental Chile and the roots from which the Andean Cordillera juts up.

All this can be viewed from space.

Not to mention, of course, the presence of the human species: the Trans-Amazonic "highway"; at night, concentrations of light in oilfields and big cities; the gaping wounds of deforestation, the scabs of urban clusters, industrial zones, contaminated bodies of water, sedimentation…

(Ah! And the Nazca Lines, interpreted as an effort by humans to manifest their existence to distracted space travellers…)

São Paulo (22 million people), Rio de Janeiro (17 million), Buenos Aires (eleven million), Lima (over seven million), Santiago

Barú island and Bahía de Barbacoas on Colombia's
Caribbean coast. Province of Bolívar.

Col/43, page 71

(over five million), Bogotá, Caracas, Guayaquil, Quito, La Paz… Their lights shining in the night merge with the stars above… Over 300 million human beings live on South America's 18 million square kilometres: descendants –some close, others remote– of the Incas, Chibchas, Tayronas, Caribs, Araucans, Mapuches, African Negroes, of the Spaniards who arrived during the *Conquista* and Colonial periods, and, in this century, after the *Guerra Civil*. Italian, German, Turkish, Arab, Oriental immigrants… Indian cultures which still survive on the frozen Andean plateaus of Peru, Bolivia, Ecuador, in the Sierra Nevada de Santa Marta… And in the luxuriant jungles of the Amazon and Chocó… From time to time, some tribe, the existence of which the rest of mankind had been previously totally unaware, still turns up…

Twelve "independent countries" (Colombia, Venezuela, Ecuador, Peru, Bolivia, Brazil, Paraguay, Uruguay, Argentina, Chile, Surinam and Guyana) and two "colonial possessions" (French Guyana and the Falkland Islands), the outlines of which cannot be discerned or glimpsed from space… only on political maps, in consulates and border posts between one country and another.

III

Among these countries, five are known today as *Bolivariano:* Colombia, Venezuela, Ecuador, Peru and Bolivia.

They could fit into one single space photograph, as they fitted in the mind of the *Libertador* when he wrote his *Carta de Jamaica:* "It is a grandiose idea to attempt to form one single nation from the new world, with one single bond uniting its parts between them and with the whole".

However, Bolívar never lived to see them all together, at the same time, from above, not even when the legendary hero ascended to the glacial summit of the Chimborazo (the same peak climbed in 1802 by the great Humboldt, convinced at the time that it was the highest mountain on Earth).

But we can. We can see, in one sweeping glance from a spaceship, the five countries which form the north-western curve of the continent, and which were born as independent nations thanks precisely to the visionary tenacity of *Libertador* Simón Bolívar.

With a close-up from space, we could spot the highest sources of rivers which spring up in the Andean stretches of the *Bolivariano* countries and irrigate the Amazon region, and which to a certain extent contribute to the lasting bio-diversity of the planet's largest

Dry valley of the altiplano in the cold
and barren deserts of northern Chile.

Chi/178, page 206

24

rain forest. We would understand why the accelerated deforestation of Andean mountains represents for the Amazon as great a threat as the felling of its own tropical trees.

We would discover the *páramos,* ecosystems which only exist in this corner of the Earth. From these moss-incrusted moors gush forth the limpid waters which make life possible in Colombia and parts of Venezuela and Ecuador.

We would see the snow line in the higher Andes recede at a disquieting pace, a phenomenon related locally to mountain slope deforestation, and on the planetary level to the so-called "global hothouse effect"… which, in plain language, means that there's increasingly less snow on the snowcaps.

We could come to understand the effects of the *El Niño* phenomenon on the coasts and hinterlands of Peru, Ecuador and Colombia.

We would contemplate the humid and dry punas (vegetal formations on Andean altiplanos and slopes which, according to Peruvian and Bolivian ecologists, "range from continuous grasslands to steppes of discontinuous scrub, of resinous and thorny plants"), the *suni* ("transition geosystems between cold and temperate punas", such as the shores of Lake Titicaca), the humid and dry *yungas* (ecosystems situated between 800 and 2,000 m. above sea level), the parched deserts of the Peruvian coast, the aforementioned jungles of Chocó…

"If men are different", said Francisco José de Caldas in an essay on these lands entitled *Del Influjo del Clima sobre los Seres Organizados* (a pioneering text on ecology, written in 1808, many decades before the word was coined in Germany and almost two centuries before biodiversity became a topic in America), "the Andean vegetation seems to verge on extremes. Within the short span of twenty leagues the observant botanist finds plants similar to specimens in Siberia, the Alps, Bengal and southern Tartary. By descending a mere 5,000 yards", Caldas continues, "one passes from polar moss to equatorial jungle. Two inches more on the barometer are enough to change the face of the flora realm. Balsams, resins, fragrances, poisons, antidotes, all potent (medicinal) virtues are omnipresent throughout our magnificent Cordillera. Cereals, vegetables, meadow plants, with their generous properties, flourish on its slopes. On the higher reaches, pulses, mosses and most of the cryptogamia have taken refuge. Here, one again finds potent (medicinal) virtues in some plants. As we have said before, extremes meet. How different are the forests of Santiago from those in the environs of Quito! The height of trees increases in inverted proportion to the altitude of the soil where they grow.

The Meta flowing into the Orinoco,
on the border between Colombia and Venezuela.

Ven/60, page 77

On the coasts, they are colossal, their diameter enormous, their trunks erect, perpendicular, and leave wide spaces between them. Climbing plants abound in the extreme. Lianas, resembling cables of a large ship, climb up and down, some perpendicular, others winding in spirals around tree trunks. Here they form caverns, and there roofs that the fiery rays of the sun fail to penetrate. Palms, these proud champions of the steaming jungles, lift up into the air their majestic foliage and tower over all that surrounds them. Moss seldom covers their trunks. Ground roots stretch horizontally over prodigious distances. (…) Trees in the higher Cordillera are pigmies compared to those below. The latter soar to forty, fifty and frequently sixty yards high; the former never exceed ten, fifteen or at the most twenty. Their roots grow deep and withstand the violence of the winds blowing in these lofty places. Their trunks are close to each other, twisted and entirely incrusted with moss. Creepers are infinitely scarce. Here the Pothos abound, and titilandcias (sic) and other parasitic specimens (sic). One single high palm tree, others small, maintain at high altitudes the form of their counterparts, which seem to grow lavishly in the hot plains…"

End of quote…

What is left of this today in the *Bolivariano* countries? When one knows that, in the past decade, devastation affected 0.54% of South America's forests, where for every hectare reforested (generally with foreign species), between ten and 15 hectares of native forest are cut down. And that, according to the United Nations Program for the Environment (PNUMA), 70% of productive lands in Mexico and South America are suffering, to one degree or another, from the process of turning into desert, and 47% of pasture zones are losing their fertility due to bungling management.

In the document *Nuestra Propia Agenda,* the Commission of Development and Environment for Latin America and the Caribbean warns that the region contains 40% of the world's tropical forest animal and plant species, but at the present rate of devastation, within 40 years between 100,000 and 350,000 species are expected to have disappeared. "In various parts", to quote the report, "the local diet came from autochtonous crops adapted to climatic particularities, but these crops have dwindled by more than half in favour of processed grains and other foods. (…) Of the 250,000 species of superior plants, 90,000 are found in tropical Latin America. If we consider that ten percent of these have medicinal properties, another ten percent industrial uses and that another 15% are edible, we have 31,500 useful species available. In the late seventies, only one percent of the estimated 50,000 angiosperm species from the Brazilian Amazon had been studied to analyze their chemical composition. (…) Approximately a thousand Amazon plant

Coastal desert and town of Tumbes in northern Peru,
near the frontier with Ecuador.

Per/81, page 126

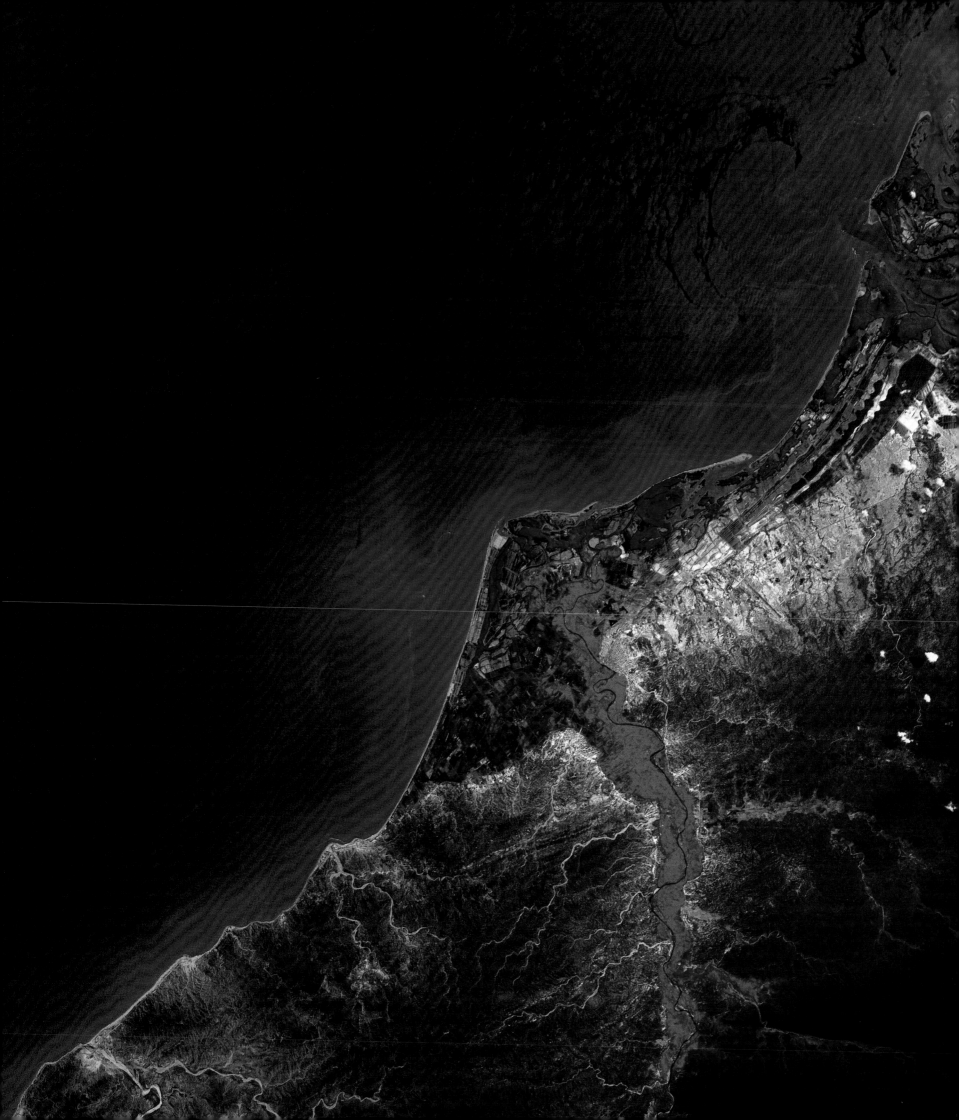

species are potentially cultivable, and at least 300 arboreal species would prove invaluable for reforestation. In Andean mountainous zones, 225 species are potentially cultivable, and 45 animal species are potentially breedable or usable".

IV

The worldwide tendency to shape blocs of integration, which surreptitiously transcends national borders, has not emerged in most cases as the result of ecological consciousness of the artificiality of frontiers and of the need to administer ecosystems by taking into account their natural features and not the "scars of history" (as is the case of the so-called "Amazon Pact"), but as the result of unabashed commercial greed and the necessity of strengthening regional and subregional economies in order to compete with economic blocs from other horizons of the planet.

The countries of Latin America, and particularly the *Bolivariano* countries, began, in 1966, a process of trade integration which culminated, in 1969, in the so-called "Cartagena Agreement", initially ratified by Colombia, Ecuador, Peru, Bolivia and Chile; Venezuela formally adhered years later (and Chile withdrew…).

The agreement's formal goals are the coordination of economic and social policies and of national legislations which institutionalize and back them, the adoption of common policies on tariffs, intellectual property, foreign capital investments and, in general, opening-up of markets. The *Bolivariano* countries, which for all aforementioned purposes form the so-called Andean Group or Pact, oversee the Cartagena Agreeement through a Commission (the Cartagena Agreement's highest authority), a Board or technical branch composed by three members, a Consultative Committee, an Economic and Social Adviser Committee formed by businessmen and workers from member countries and an Andean Court of Justice. Cartagena Agreement member countries also created the *Corporación Andina de Fomento* (CAF), "a multinational company of an eminently public nature aimed at granting technical and financial support to concrete projects connected with the subregional market".

Many are the acronyms denoting the trade integration efforts of Latin American countries: the MCCA (Central American Common Market), the ALALC (Latin American Free Trade Association), the ALADI (Latin American Association for Integration), the MERCOSUR (Common Market formed by Argentina, Brazil, Paraguay and Uruguay), the G-3 or Group of Three (Mexico, Colombia and Vene-

Bahía de Tumaco on Colombia's Pacific coast,
in the province of Nariño, near the frontier with Ecuador.

Col/69, page 123

zuela), and others of a prominently scientific and cultural nature, such as the *Convenio Andrés Bello*. The dominant trend of internationalization of the economy, with all its dangers and possibilities, and technological hardware stemming especially from computer sciences, which favour the existence of networks such as CETCOL (Colombian Science, Education and Technology System) or the *Red Caldas* (thus named in honour of the Colombian scientist from the beginning of the past century, whose pioneer ecological writings we quoted above in a few paragraphs), linking Colombian scientists working in around 20 countries. The integration of these networks with similar ones in other countries of the planet gradually contributes to surmount the previously formidable obstacle of national frontiers. Possibly indeed, much is still to be accomplished before completely overcoming differences between countries. And it certainly proves positive that, while on one hand consciousness increases of the oneness of Planet Earth and the human race, on the other hand and in a simultaneous manner, the urge grows to strengthen local identities: unity in diversity and vice versa.

V

The America that Bolívar dreamed to see converted into "the world's greatest nation, less for its extension and wealth than for its freedom and for its grandeur", is an enormous island between two immense oceans, which represents 12% of land surface on Planet Earth. A continent which remained hidden to Europeans until only five hundred years ago.

As it still remains hidden to the majority of us who continue to see it from within, from the ground, incapable of linking "its parts between them and with the whole" (and not as Bolívar and Caldas and Humboldt and the man from Neguá managed to see it from above, their minds overpowering the force of gravity which anchored them to Earth).

To look at the continent from space, as God beheld it on the seventh day of Creation, and as we can see it today, with the eyes of an extraterrestrial traveller, helps us to understand it, to understand ourselves as a whole. For America. For the planet. For this Universe, with which we, children of the Earth, share the will to live.

GUSTAVO WILCHES-CHAUX

Border between Bolivia and Brazil, west and east of the lakes,
a hundred kilometres north of the town of Corumbá.

Bra/162, page 201

Images from Satellite

he history of aerospace remote sensing is recent, but full of triumphs. As a scientific tool, it has allowed to discover new fields of study of our planet, in a more extensive and efficient manner. Despite its purely scientific use, from the artistic viewpoint it also offers wonderful visions of the "blue planet". What would become, in the second half of the 20th century, aerospace remote sensing, began in empirical fashion with the loading of photographic equipment on planes. Developed during the First World War and perfected during the Second World War, this technique will be progressively pursued because of the importance given by the conquest of space to methods of remote sensing, especially thanks to computer graphics. The first great concepts of space remote sensing were born in the early sixties in the United States and the Soviet Union. From the seventies onwards, the French and Canadians begin to spread this image culture with their own technology. Thus, the task of inventing this new science, practically from scratch, proved incumbent to the pioneers of observation of the Earth from space.

The idea of launching military observation satellites was born in the early days of space conquest with the United States SAMOS (Satellite and Missile Observation System) project. The first of such satellites, destined to replace U2 spy-planes, went into orbit January 31, 1961. But the story actually begins with a Soviet astronautical feat: on October 4, 1957, the history-making Sputnik was launched, a small artificial satellite of 84 kg. In comparison, the first American satellite, Explorer-1, launched in January 1958, only weighed 14 kg. Later come satellites of the TIROS (Television Infrared Observation Satellite) type, and on April 1, 1960, TIROS-1 takes the

Salar de Atacama and town of San Pedro de Atacama,
on the San Pedro river.

Chi/182, page 206

first picture of the terrestrial globe. The first three TIROS took thousands of pictures of Earth, some of them incredible revelations for meteorology. Each country follows its own program: the Soviets with Sputnik and Vostok, the Americans with Mercury. In May 1960, the former manage to launch a 4,500 kg. space station, and on April 12, 1961, the Soviet Yuri Gagarin becomes the first spaceman. On February 20, 1962, on board Mercury Friendship-7, the American Scott Glenn completes three revolutions around the Earth.

Thus, the first flights with human passengers proceed, and, little by little, with descriptions from the human eye alone, details and colours of the continents seen from space gain in accuracy. In 1963, an article written by Robert N. Colwell reveals the potential advantages and drawbacks of satellite photography. He demonstrated that, among significant specific scientific applications, the inventory of natural resources was the most interesting.

To all astronauts, Planet Earth appears haloed by a blue transparent layer. The atmosphere acts as a blurry element where radiations resolve into a blue coloration of light. The blue colour of the sky, seen from the ground as well as from space, is attributed to this phenomenon. For this reason, the astronauts have called our Earth the "blue planet".

The first photographs of Earth were taken directly from the spaceship by the crew with a normal camera. On June 3, 1965, the American Edward H. White leaves the cabin into the cosmic void for 20 minutes and takes several pictures of Earth.

These photographs, taken with a Hasselblad camera, as part of the NASA (National Aeronautics and Space Administration) GEMINI program, reveal terrestrial forms and structures previously ill-known, such as the Bay of California fault, and volcanic lava fields and craters of over 500 km.2 in Mexico, which had never been discovered before. The GEMINI program managed to take 1,464 colour photographs of Earth. The precision and sharpness of these pictures show the overwhelming advantage of shots taken directly in space. The apex and progressive development of aerospace remote sensing concepts run parallel to the triumphs of space conquest. "Remote sensing", an American term designating this new technique of detection from a distance, was coined in 1961. The concept gave birth to the EROS (Earth Resources Observation Systems) program, created in 1966 to apply remote sensing techniques to the inventory, observation and administration of natural resources.

With the launching, on July 26, 1972, of terrestrial observation satellite ERTS-1 (Earth Resources Technology Satellite, named LANDSAT) and the transmission of its first pictures, remote sensing achieves worldwide recognition. Thanks to this satellite, we had to totally revise the system of geographic information used previously. With this technique, we can carry out statistical research

Vast slopes of the Bolivian Cordillera Real's eastern foothills,
preceding the Chaco shrublands.

Bol/170, page 203

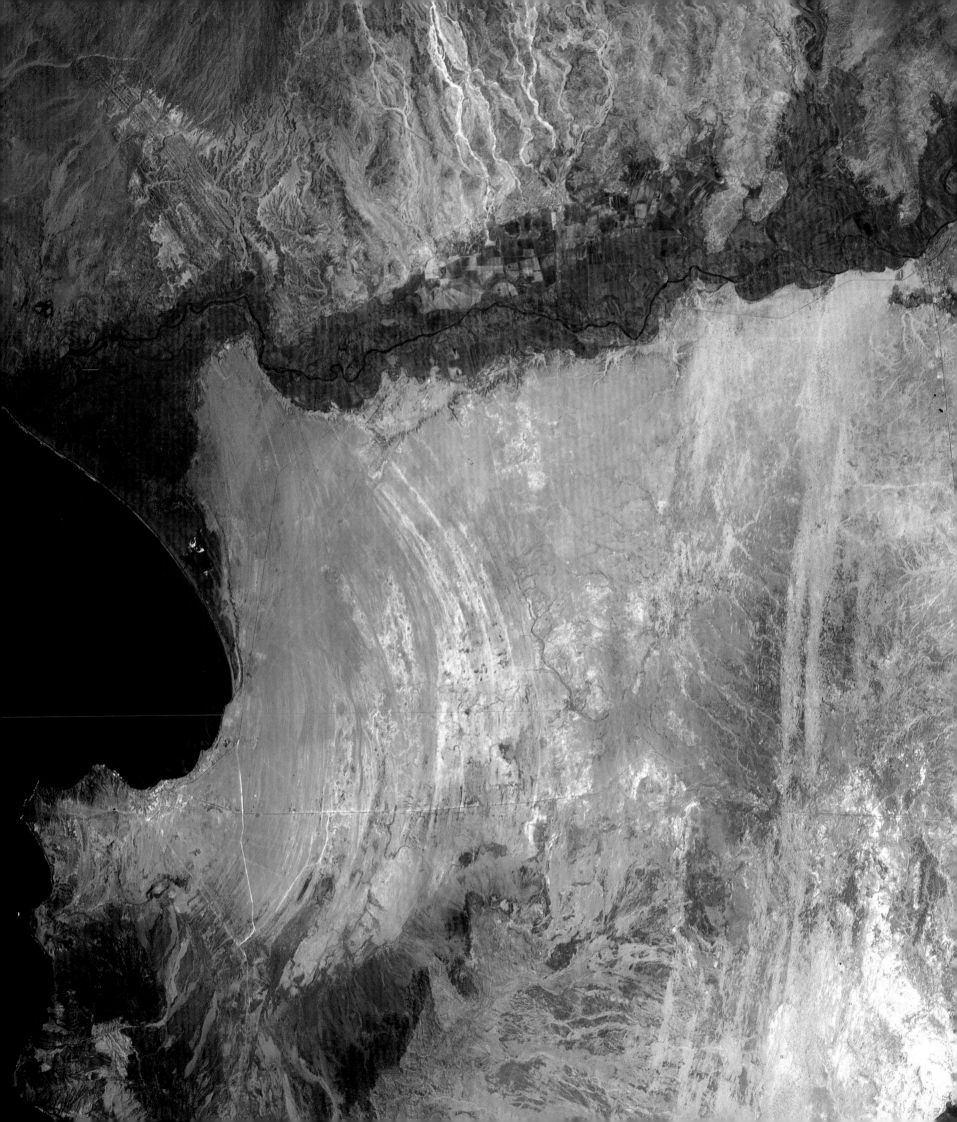

which analyzes, at the same time, occupation of territory at ground level and human activities upon it. It's a dynamic means of research, which enables to go beyond statistical data such as cadastre, files and surveys. A satellite will give specific information to each branch of geography.

By the means of their national agencies, Americans NASA and NOAA (National Oceanic and Atmospheric Administration) and Europeans ASE (Agence Spatiale Européenne) and CNES (Centre National d'Études Spatiales) have placed, on different terrestrial orbits, various series of satellites for civilian use. Natural resource satellites such as LANDSAT and SPOT, whose orbits are circular, quasi-polar and heliosynchronous. Meteorological satellites, geostationary in relation to the equatorial divide, such as METEOSAT. Or quasi-polar orbit satellites, such as NOAA, TIROS and NIMBUS. And finally oceanographic satellites, such as SEASAT.

Launched, like the first, in the early seventies, all these satellites reflect the aspiration to enhance knowledge of Earth's natural phenomena and anticipate related human responses.

From this recent and successful history, an original and innovative technique was born, aerospace remote sensing, with its new tools for new applications. It's necessary to be acquainted with various notions about the functioning of terrestrial observation satellites to better understand the purpose of such a technique. Unlike spy-satellites, of exclusively military use, terrestrial observation satellites have multiple applications in the civilian field.

The working principle is almost always the same and consists in recording, by means of appropriate sensors, the dynamic phenomena of the Earth's atmosphere or the natural and human phenomena on its surface. The satellite not only takes photographs but also records, thanks to a radiometer, the luminous signal reflected by each terrestrial object after being struck by sunlight. The sensors thus codify mathematically, under the form of numbers, the "solar signature" of each object, send it to a powerful computer on the ground, which interprets it and creates images. In this fashion, the final product is not a photograph but an image which has specific colours corresponding to spectral signatures. For example, the sea appears black, the vegetation in different shades of red according to the intensity of development and the cities in grey. Colours appear in this manner because the numeric data gathered are rendered in particular shades based on an appropriate codification.

The description or interpretation process of an image is almost always the same and allows to "see" and decipher everything shown by the image according to the purpose of the user. Before looking at the image itself, one has to read the technical information

Bahía de Paita and estuary of the Chira river
in northern Peru's coastal desert.

Per/86, page 128

located on the panel. Conventionally, the upper part presents the satellite's name and number, which indicates the generation of technique utilized. Afterwards, the technical recording channel is registered, for instance HRV 2, namely High Visual Resolution Channel 2. It can be Thermic Infrared or another channel of the visual range. Also appearing are the image's geographic location references in relation to a special classification of the launching entity, in the French case CNES (Centre National d'Études Spatiales), on the satellite's flight pattern covering the entire world. There are light ratio panels in black-and-white above, and in colour below.

Afterwards, the technical characteristics of each radiometric channel used are examined; a graphic scale of the image is installed to allow the location of each object and measure its actual size. On the lower part appear characteristics of geographic position of the centre of the image with reference to geographic coordinates (in degrees and minutes), and then other technical data specifying corrections printed on the image to make it legible. As a formality, the hour the picture was taken and the logo of the company owning rights to the satellite are also displayed. Now, with all this preliminary information, one can geographically and technically locate the region to be detailed.

The next step is analysis of the image from a geographical point of view. This analysis generally comprises two parts: a physical commentary and a human study.

Physical commentary locates the zone in terms of coastline, mountain, desert, urban area or jungle. It indicates the names of the major orographical and hydrographical features as well as the prevailing type of soil usage: woodland, city, pasture, etc… Human study brings additional information on the type of human activity and occupation: agriculture, cattle raising, and additional observations on factors not apparent in the image, concerning the zone's history: the reasons why a city, canal, road network or form of agriculture were established: geometric fields or the anarchy of burnt patches revealing recent settlement.

It's important to relate what can be seen in the picture with the evolution of human presence, in order to deduce a logic pattern behind human settlement on a given territory. By verifying if the zone is colonized or not, and taking its history into account, one can draw conclusions on its future. There are satellites with other purposes than terrestrial observation. The first satellites had meteorological functions, now performed by the American NOAA and European METEOSAT. The role of these satellites, on geostationary orbits, is to follow the evolution of cloud masses over oceans and continents. One can infer from the recurrence of such atmospheric phenomena the weather conditions in a specific zone, as well as meteorological calamities such as cyclones.

*Course of the Apure river
in the Venezuelan Llanos. State of Apure.*

Ven/35, page 69

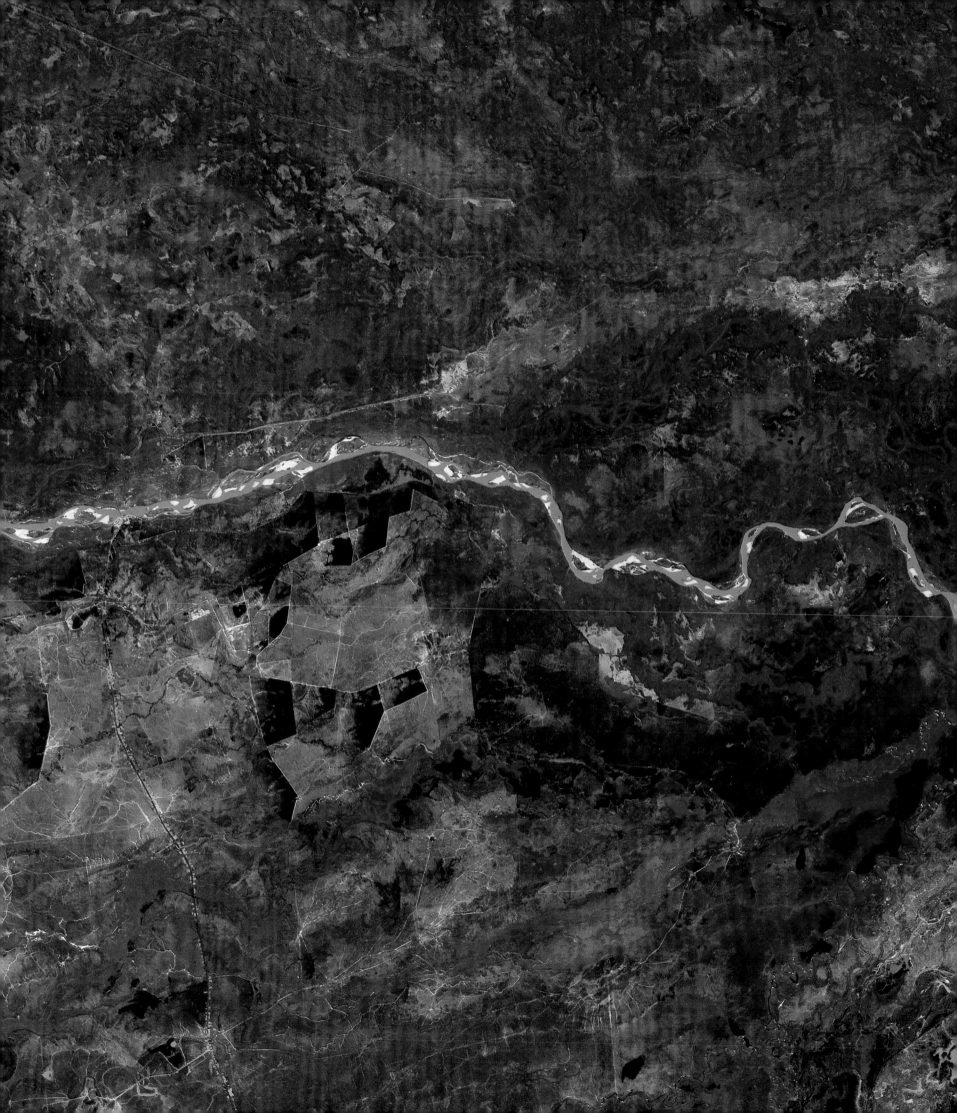

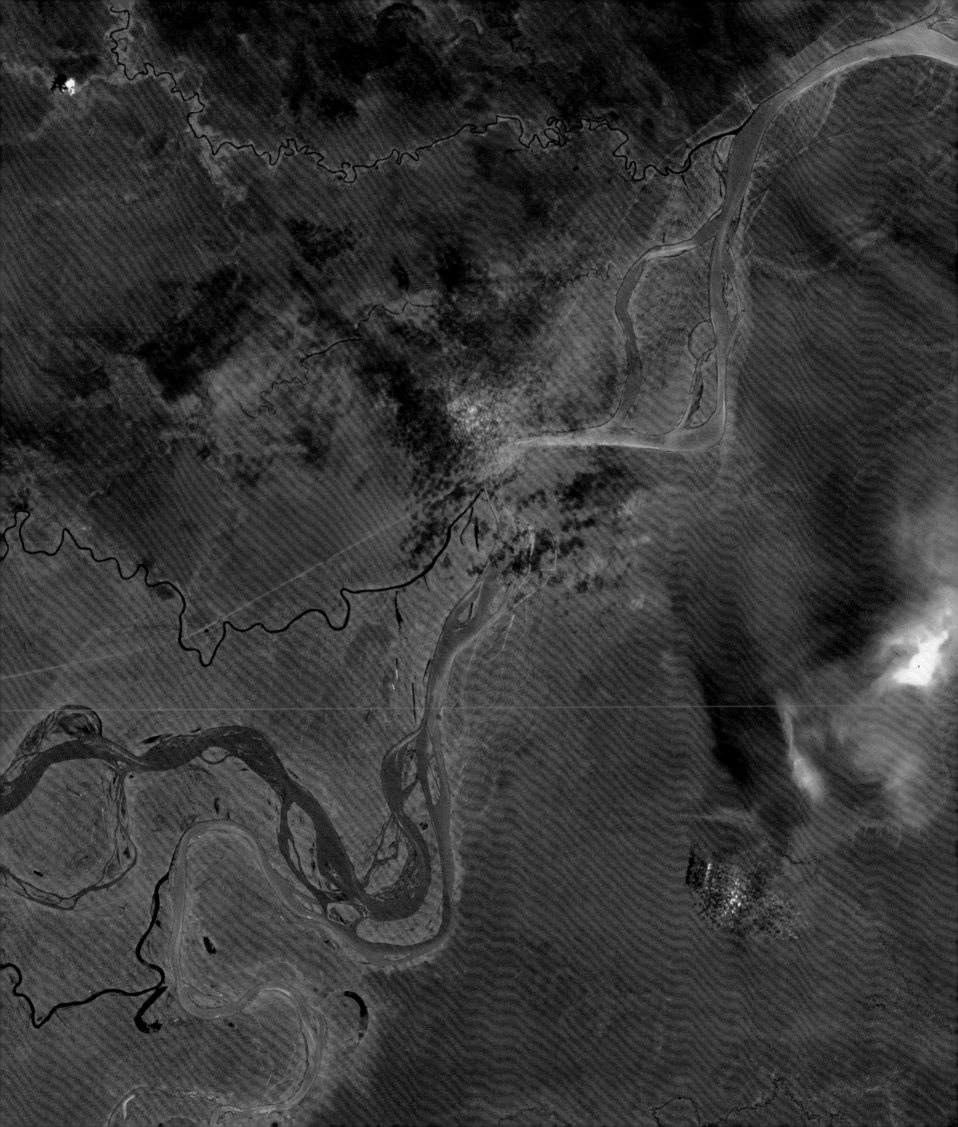

The SEASAT satellite, launched in 1978 by NASA to replace NOAA, from an altitude of 800 km. analyzes, with high-capacity thermic infrared radiometers, phenomena occuring on the surface of the sea through temperature contrasts. Over the past 20 years, a total of eleven NOAA satellites have been in constant operation. Natural resource satellites such as SPOT or LANDSAT have circular, quasi-polar orbits, and are heliosynchronous: in other words, they always follow the sun to enjoy light in the zone of observation. The first LANDSAT was launched in 1972, and the first SPOT in February 1986. Despite this time gap, they have practically the same characteristics: they are located at an altitude of over 800 km. on circular, quasi-polar orbits; LANDSAT features more spectral bands than SPOT (six instead of three), but has an inferior ground detail accuracy (30 metres instead of ten), and LANDSAT covers a 10,000 km² territory against SPOT's 3,600 to 4,800 km².

Thus, numerous applications permit a new and global vision of the environment. Indeed, since the eighties, aerospace remote sensing bears its mark on the great events of our time. Apart from its obvious cartographic role, which allows to update the maps of unknown zones without costly field research (highly precise cartography on a large scale, up to 1/50,000, with contour lines and georeferential points thanks to the Global Positioning System), computer processing of numeric data, in the form of tapes, with powerful programs such as Multiscope or Arc Info, also enable to develop countless kinds of research. Moreover, it can be used to locate an abnormal source of radiation, such as the Tchernobyl nuclear plant explosion in 1986, which was detected by the West thanks to space remote sensing; to assess the extension of severe floods of the Ganges river in Bangladesh; or, beginning in 1979, to measure the deterioration of the ozone layer. It also helps to scrutinize imperceptible movements of the Earth's crust. In this manner, many steps forward in the scientific realm stem from its use, with the promise of further great developments, because the evolution of the world and the terrestrial environment has been extremely rapid, and to keep up with the times proves much more exacting.

In this respect, one must mention deforestation, which affects the entire intertropical belt, the growing deserts of the tropical zone, and, on a more general level, the degradation of the atmosphere on a planetary scale. One can also study the modification of coastlines or riverbeds due to human tampering or natural cataclysms.

The hothouse phenomenon, caused by changes in the gas content of the atmosphere, can have catastrophic consequences for mankind's survival over the next 20 to 50 years. If temperature and sea level rise, thus wreaking havoc in climatic zones, agricultural production and occupation of lowlands (delta regions for instance) will be seriously affected. Thanks to measures taken by satellite,

Confluence of the Huallaga and Marañón rivers
in the Peruvian Amazon jungle.

Per/91, page 130

one can foresee, on an average-term basis, with the help of mathematical models, alterations in temperature, vegetation growth and icecap surface.

In this fashion, the spreading of deserts, especially in semi-arid regions, can be studied with great accuracy in relation to climate, vegetal and animal biomass, soil, water and human activity. As climatic stations are very scarce in such areas, where brutal weather changes make extrapolation strenuous, images from meteorological satellites such as METEOSAT, METEOR or INSAT offer highly useful information on surface temperatures, velocity and direction of cloud systems, as well as atmospheric humidity.

Satellite data also prove instrumental to gather further knowledge on vegetal biomass and chlorophyll activity, thanks to vegetation indicators, which are classifications of the different types of trees in a zone, and their stages of growth. The difficulty in arid regions resides in establishing the difference between dry and green vegetation. In this case, it's necessary to have data of the terrain obtained from field work, to match with those from the satellite orbiting above.

Inventory of the world's major forests (the Amazon jungle and the conifer woods of cold zones) is one of the prominent challenges in this end of the century. With thorough knowledge of these zones of difficult access, one can better prognosticate their vulnerable points and, consequently, exploit them in a more rational manner. Within the framework of preservation of resources, terrestrial observation satellites are essential to make better use of halieutic (fishing) resources. One can determine where the various species live and breed, the movements of shoals in order to protect, or exploit, them. Thanks to thermal sensors, aerospace remote sensing helps to find vast deposits potentially rich in oil or useful or rare energy-yielding minerals. Finally, detrimental human activities, and particularly man-induced fires, which heavily contribute to spread desert areas, can be easily detected by satellite pictures.

But deforestation is not caused solely by these factors; many other combining elements intervene. To prevent them, permanent interchange between satellite data and ground information on the area investigated is called for. In respect to territorial demarcation, the satellite's "eye" contributes immensely to decision-making on tracing a new road or giving local authorities various alternatives for optimum urban development.

Aerospace remote sensing allows to research and remedy other pernicious aspects of human activity: for example, pollution in its manifold forms. Substantial damage can be located, tracked and counteracted, such as an oil spill at sea, or the health of a vegetal species threatened by human industry can be diagnosed. The good or bad condition of forests is determined by registering

Tropical rain forest in north-eastern Bolivia,
course of the Maniquí river and town of San Borja.

Bol/148, page 197

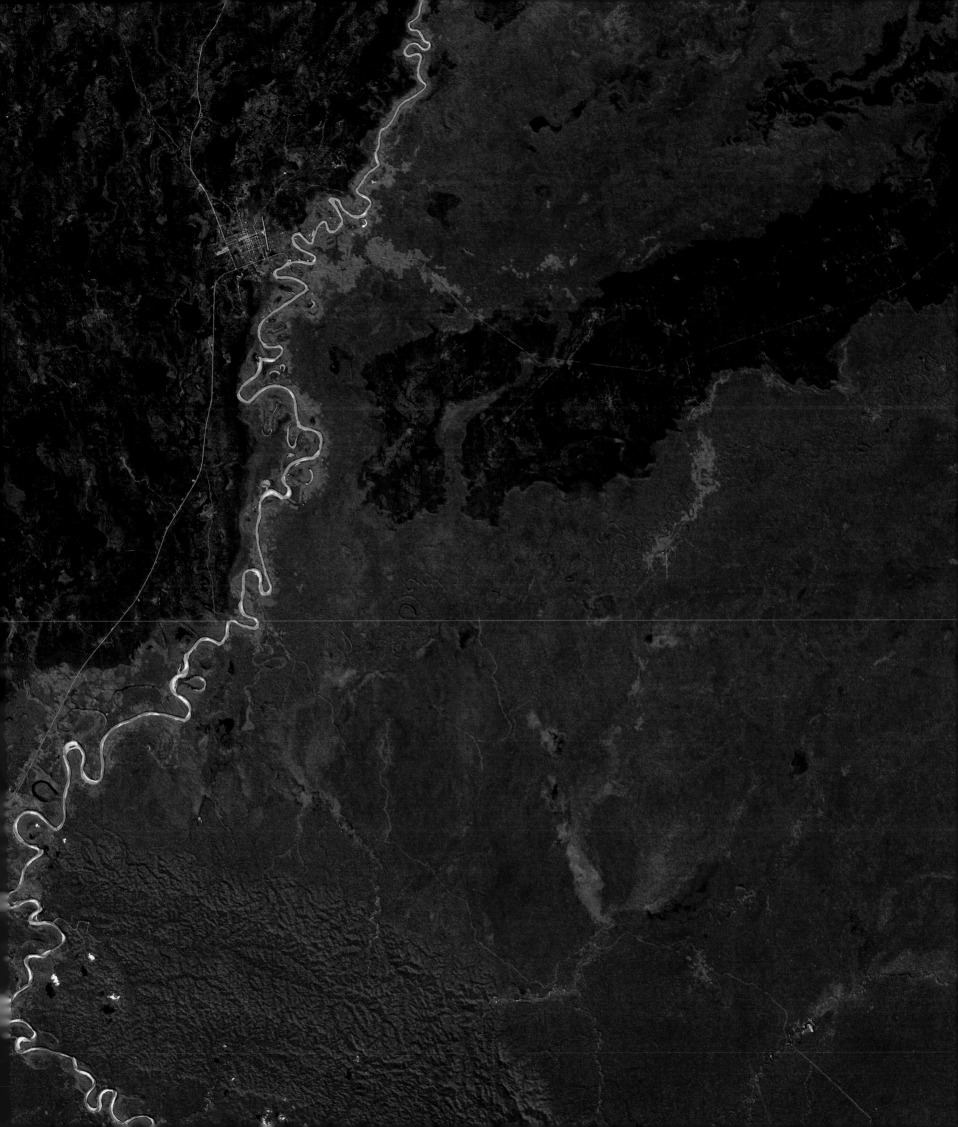

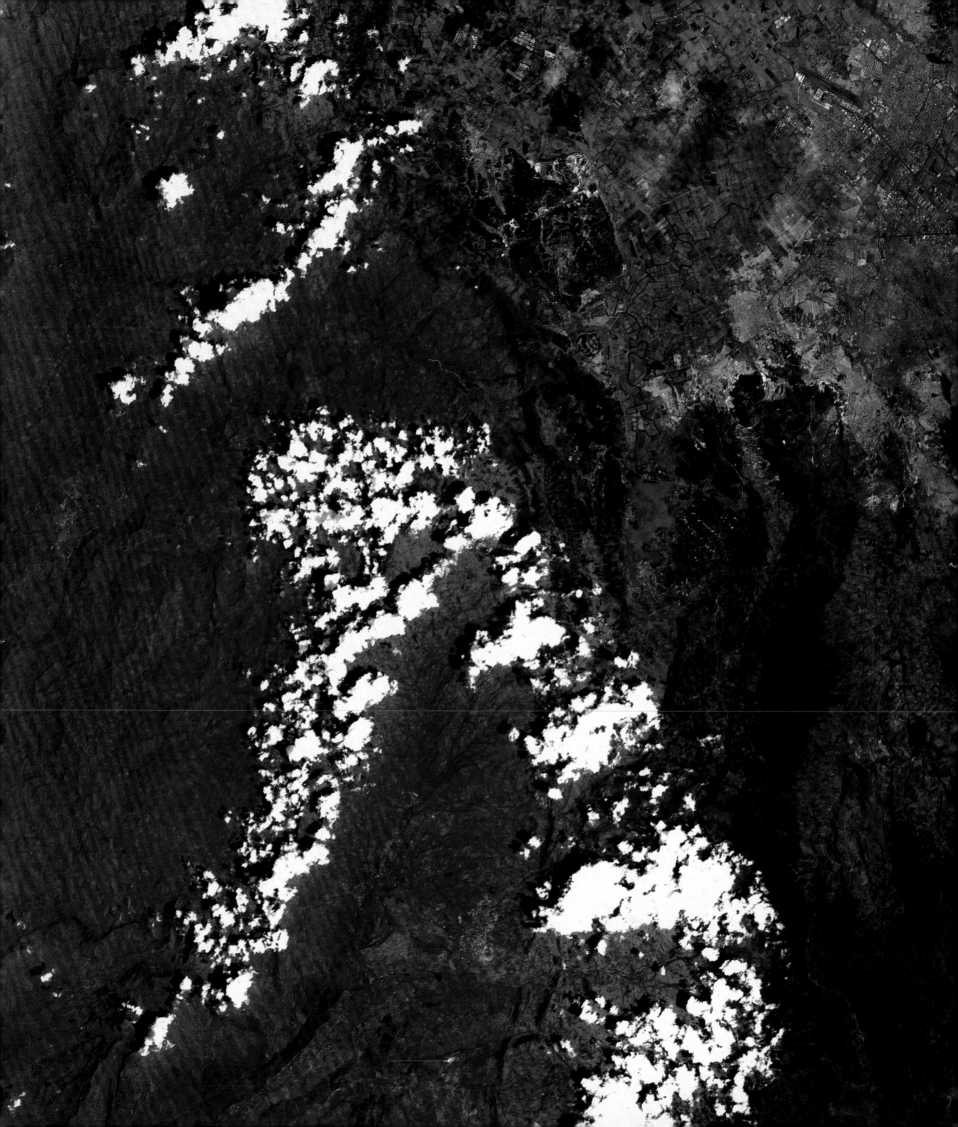

chlorophyll activity level. In Latin America, several utilizations have been applied in government or private enterprise projects, involving considerable work. Thus the consequences of a construction project can be anticipated before an irreparable situation occurs. In the case of Colombia's *Troncal del Caribe* motorway, which obliterated the marshlands between Santa Marta and Barranquilla, perhaps it would have been possible to consider another route or realize, during the construction phase, before it was too late, the vast degradation inflicted upon this coastal woodland environment. Regional cartographic studies to determine the size of the coral reef and avoid pollution in the Rosario archipelago have also been accomplished with satellite assistance.

In Mexico, SPOT has succeeded in updating on a very large scale the cartography of the entire nation. Such an endeavour, which would have taken years of aerial surveys, was achieved in a few months with a reliability and accuracy beyond the reach of the photographic camera. Furthermore, the satellite, in constant operation, enables a permanent renewal of cartographic data without the need to undertake another costly survey. In Mexico, the problem of unbridled urban growth is also controlled by SPOT. In Argentina, the comparison of satellite data with property deeds has contributed to a revised cadastre for a more rational use of land, and helped the government to ascertain which land belongs to whom and claim from owners taxes in accordance with their actual estate. Flood damage in the Buenos Aires area has also been investigated by satellite. In Brazil, this method has evaluated the environmental impact of the construction of a pipeline, the erosion of hillsides and deforestation, and regulated the granting of credit to sugar manufacturers, to restrict unchecked, soil-depleting plantation of sugarcane. In Venezuela, it is used to carry out cadastre inventories prior to oil prospection ventures, and helped to appraise the magnitude of the world's greatest bauxite deposit. In Peru, satellite images serves for mining surveys and the study of dormant volcanic activity. In Honduras, SPOT keeps tabs on the progress rate in road restoration works financed by the World Bank. Chile and Bolivia resort to satellite pictures to resolve land litigations.

Other applications, on the private level, have equal importance. Oil and mining companies utilize satellite images to determine preferential survey and excavation areas. Thus time and money are saved by reducing field prospecting work.

As for territorial demarcation, pictures taken from orbit provide data enabling simulation models of road routes or housing developments, with environmental concern in mind. Detrimental impact of such projects on the environment can thus be assessed, and a *juste milieu* determined.

Santa Fe de Bogotá, the Colombian capital,
in the Sabana de Bogotá. Province of Cundinamarca.

Col/55, page 75

Thanks to SPOT's outstanding performance, cartographic data have been expanded and improved to near-perfection all over the world. We can now map every point of the Earth's surface. A resolution of up to ten metres at ground level, which enables minute detail, has created high-quality cartography on a large scale. The stereoscopic process makes it possible to work in three dimensions and the mirror system obtains repeated shots without having to pass vertically over the point to be mapped. Indeed, this technological tool has revolutionized the technique of cartography and mankind's perception of his home planet.

From an utilitarian point of view, SPOT applications prove numerous, not to say infinite, the only limit being that of territorial planning projects.

If one attempted to find a common denominator for SPOT applications in South America, it would not be a question of scientifically defining the different projects achieved, but rather of observing the field of research which unfolds under the satellite's "eye". The great particularity of South America is to be a "hidden" continent.

Indeed, its surface is masked by a ceiling of clouds hovering more or less permanently over most jungle and several mountain areas. This "lid", which conceals mankind's activities on the ground, can explain, just as in the case of sub-equatorial Africa, the relatively-reduced utilization of the 1.8 tons of highly-sophisticated technology carried by SPOT.

To this natural particularity, one must also add general lack of awareness of the immense advantages afforded by this matchless instrument towards acquiring better knowledge of the environment.

Therefore, in the immediate present, development of aerospace research seems to be the realm of groups of specialists rather than nations as such; the former are often more aware of the satellite's enormous potential towards better use and preservation of our environment.

Moreover, thanks to the wealth of information provided, the international community has started to become aware of all the aforementioned problems, difficult to tackle because causes, exact circumstances and long-term effects are little-known.

We must study the progressive changes, past, present and future, of the environment, on a planetary scale. To attain this goal, 24 countries have decided to pool efforts.

Before the year 2000, the data gathered by space remote sensing on a planetary scale will allow researchers to corroborate the predictive mock-ups designed previously, and discover and understand the physical, chemical and biological interactions which

Bahía de Sechura on Peru's coastal desert,
south of the town of Piura.

Per/90, page 128

govern all the Earth's systems, in other words the environment which determines life. On the artistic level, and specifically in South America, the possibility arises to establish an "identity" or an originality through aerospace remote sensing, or namely, to know what's special about our continent, as seen from outer space.

In fact, each continent possibly has a physical, poetical or technical originality in respect of the use of remote sensing. This is well worth probing into. This originality exists for South America in two aspects: one thematic and artistic, the other more technical. Our continent's great originality from the thematic point of view lies in the fact that its images reveal landscapes almost untouched by the human being. Thus, lands are "virgin" because they bear few marks of human trespassing. Big cities are scarce, and the human networks of communication or housing/farming fail to leave a strong imprint on the landscape seen from space.

What could be called a unique or natural "purity", evidently has to do with the immensity of the land and, likewise, with the physical elements of the virgin terrain. Granted, because of its more recent history and sheer dimension, South America has nothing even closely resembling Europe's urban tangle, characteristic of the "old world" image from space.

Because of its size and physical elements, the continent seems empty, and vast, distinctive masses stand out in this "emptiness". The Andean Cordillera, indeed the spine of the continent, has its own spectral signature, which is the common denominator of several countries. In the same fashion, the Amazon jungle, the lung of America, also borders on several countries, and looms as a physical phenomenon unique in the world.

Thus, this relative "human emptiness" which entails the predominance of "natural" spectral signatures, such as those of the jungle or the cordillera, is a characteristic of South America on the thematic level.

As for cities, the chessboard pattern, which can be perfectly distinguished from space, may well be the essential feature of the continent's urban layout. This architectural and urbanistic quality is sufficiently repetitive to impose itself as the major human thematic element. But, with regard to cloud formations or coastlines, other tropical continents display similar spectral signatures. Therefore one cannot single out these elements as characteristic.

South America may well be, aerospatially speaking, the "natural" continent, but also the continent of natural life. In fact, its landscapes are distinguished by an abundance of vegetal life unrivaled in the world. Africa also has natural landscapes, but they are mostly deserts shaped by winds and scant rains.

The Cordillera Real, east of La Paz, where the tributaries
of the eastern jungle rivers spring. Province of La Paz.

Bol/140, page 196

The radiometric signatures of the vegetation, wherever one looks, reveal a red or green, continent, which also confirms its originality. On the technical level, a space interference, particularly active over the continent and Pacific Ocean, characterizes South America.

Thus, tiny green, blue or red points or streaks, displaying all the nuances of the rainbow, suddenly scattered at random over the images, become much more visible in a panorama of homogeneous colour such as jungle or ocean. These interferences have an original explanation. They are caused by high-energy electron and proton particles, precipitated in the atmosphere, after their "life" in a radiation belt which encircles Planet Earth be ween an altitude of 500 and 40,000 km.

This belt was discovered thanks to data transmitted by yet another satellite, the first American artificial satellite, Explorer-1, launched January 31, 1958, under the authority of physicist James Van Allen, hence the designation: "Van Allen's Belt". Massive quantities of electrons and protons are ensnared in it, in a frenzied and unrelenting swirl of motion between the North and South Poles and a longitudinal drift. Their form and stability are imparted by the power lines of the Earth's magnetic field.

Owing to their high energy, these belt particles can cause serious damage to spaceships and crews. This is one of the reasons why manned vessels never go beyond an altitude of 500 km. The SPOT satellite, orbiting at 830 km., sometimes has to bear the brunt of these particles, which erase all its accumulated data when they "die" upon disintegrating in the lower strata of the Earth's atmosphere.

Although it's not known why exactly, the Pacific and Latin American zones are the most affected by this newly-discovered phenomenon. This technical singularity, from a certain point of view, could be an artistic originality specific to our continent. It can obviously be edited out or left as such, depending on the intended use of the pictures.

So satellite images represent a powerful tool, which resorts to extremely sophisticated, and therefore expensive, space technology, but which in fact, and paradoxically, proves a very economical, unbiased and independent instrument, when one considers its benefits. The technique allows in many cases to control the costs of important construction projects, or to enforce agrarian or environmental policies. In its essence, this is a productive application, for the user, of the advances of space conquest.

In this series of pictures covering 60 km.-wide squares throughout the Andean countries, one can perceive, besides the obvious technical advantages of the instrument, a thematic unity in the continent. Flying over the Andes and the jungle, scurrying like an

Swamplands on the border between Bolivia and Brazil,
south of Corumbá. State of Mato Grosso do Sul.

Bra/157, page 200

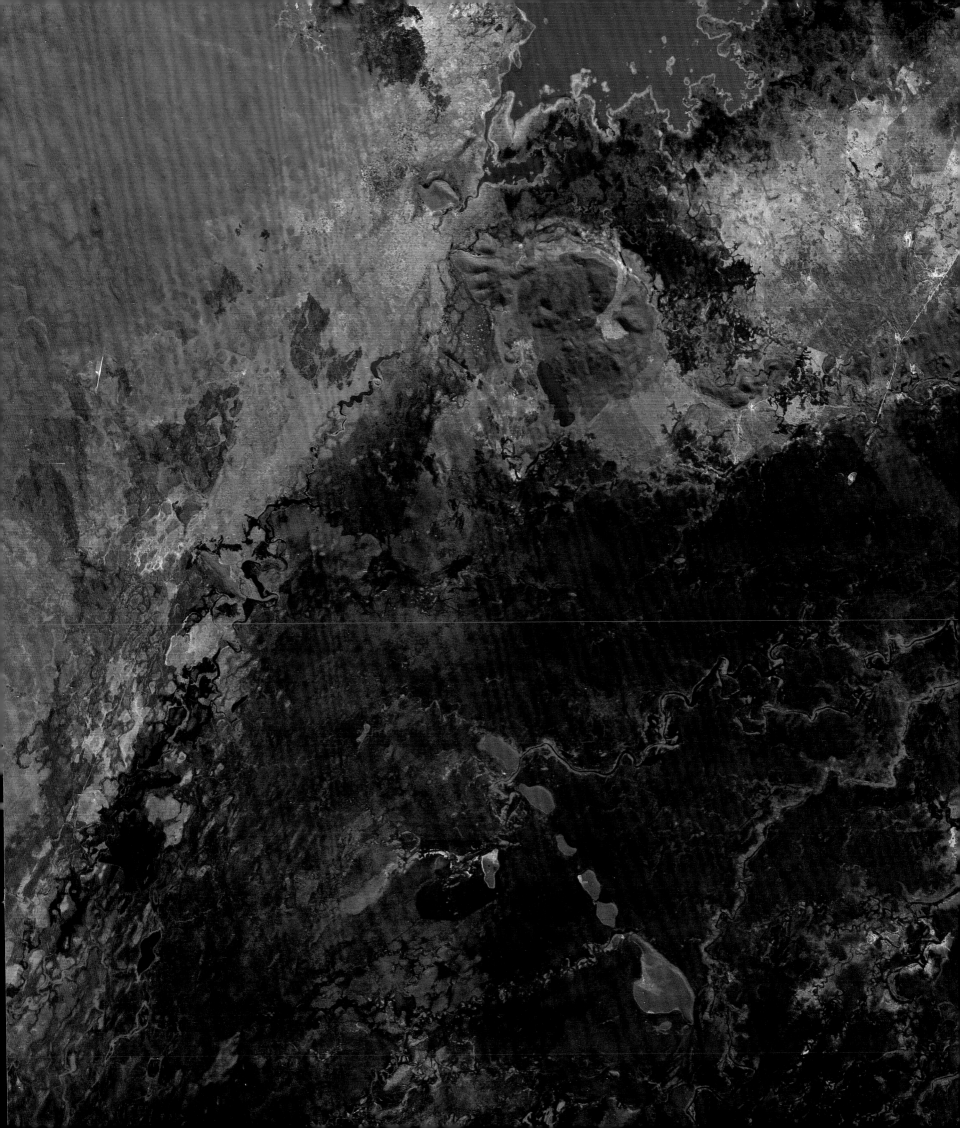

electronic crab along geographic lines, through parallels and meridians, the SPOT satellite weaves a perfect net covering the entire American continent. Oblivious of frontiers, free of all earthly restraints, this instrument, its only hindrance being clouds blocking its vision, speaks to us of Earth as an exquisite mosaic arranged in a colour code designed by its creators below.

It presents us a very tangible Earth, in a manner highly technical for some, but for others open to the creative visions of artists, and ready to put its technical marvels at the service of men of science. From a poetic viewpoint, it bestows us a vision of the Earth that we had never dreamed of.

OLIVIER BERNARD

Barren altiplano in southern Peru, near the frontier with
Bolivia and Lake Titicaca. Province of Tacna.

Per/134, page 195

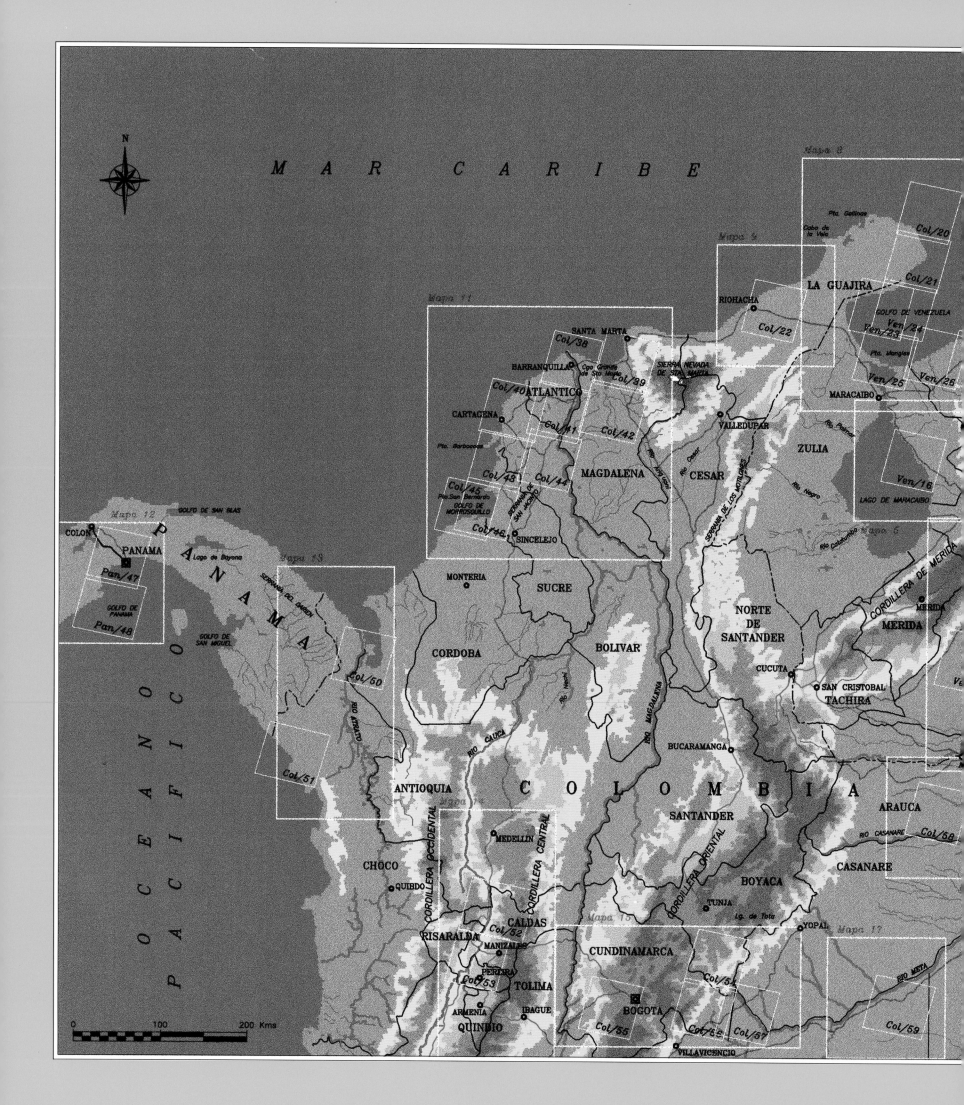

Ven/1. *The Venezuelan tropical rain forest as it merges into the Tepuyes zone. State of Bolívar. Page 80.*

One observes the transition between the jungle and zone of *Tepuyes,* which are mesetas of the Guyanese shield or pieces of the pre-Cambrian base, at over a thousand metres above the Llanos. In the western part of the picture appears the Paragua river, which flows further north into the Caroní, which in turn feeds the Guri reservoir. The white zone, to the north-west of the picture, indicates a flood-prone area, with clay or sand soils. The two rivers which cross the picture at the centre in a south-north direction are the Aza to the west and Chiguao more to the east, tributaries of the Paragua. In the eastern part of the picture one sees the Caroní river and an island. A road comes from the north, from Ciudad Bolívar, leading to the nearby small town of Canaima, the gate to the *Tepuyes* region of Roraima.

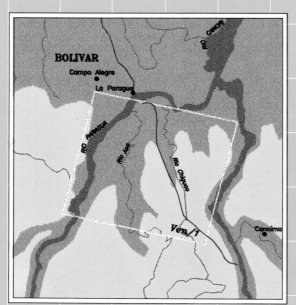

Map 1

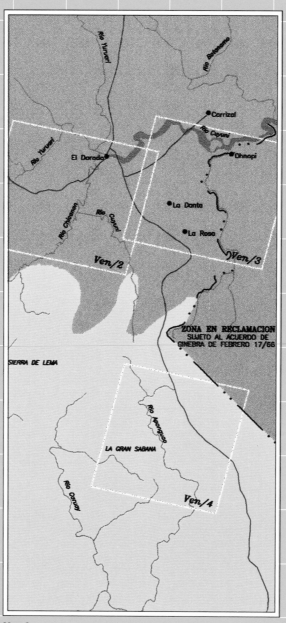

Map 2

Ven/2. *Venezuelan tropical rain forest in the state of Bolívar near the frontier with Guyana.*

The hydrographic system which can be seen in a south-north direction corresponds to the sources which feed the Cuyuni river, in the northern part of the picture, where it receives its northern tributary, the Yuruari. At this point arrives the road coming from the north which continues to the frontier with Guyana. The town at the confluence is named El Dorado, with an airstrip. Further south, along the rectilinear road, one detects human occupation by the deforested area marring the jungle. In the north-western part of the picture, the village of Ranchos Viejos displays its chessboard pattern. In a general fashion, human presence is very scarce and can only exist with a road or airstrip. From the technical point of view, one notes the effect of a divergence between the satellite's detectors, which gives a different colour to the jungle, in the form of a reddish streak.

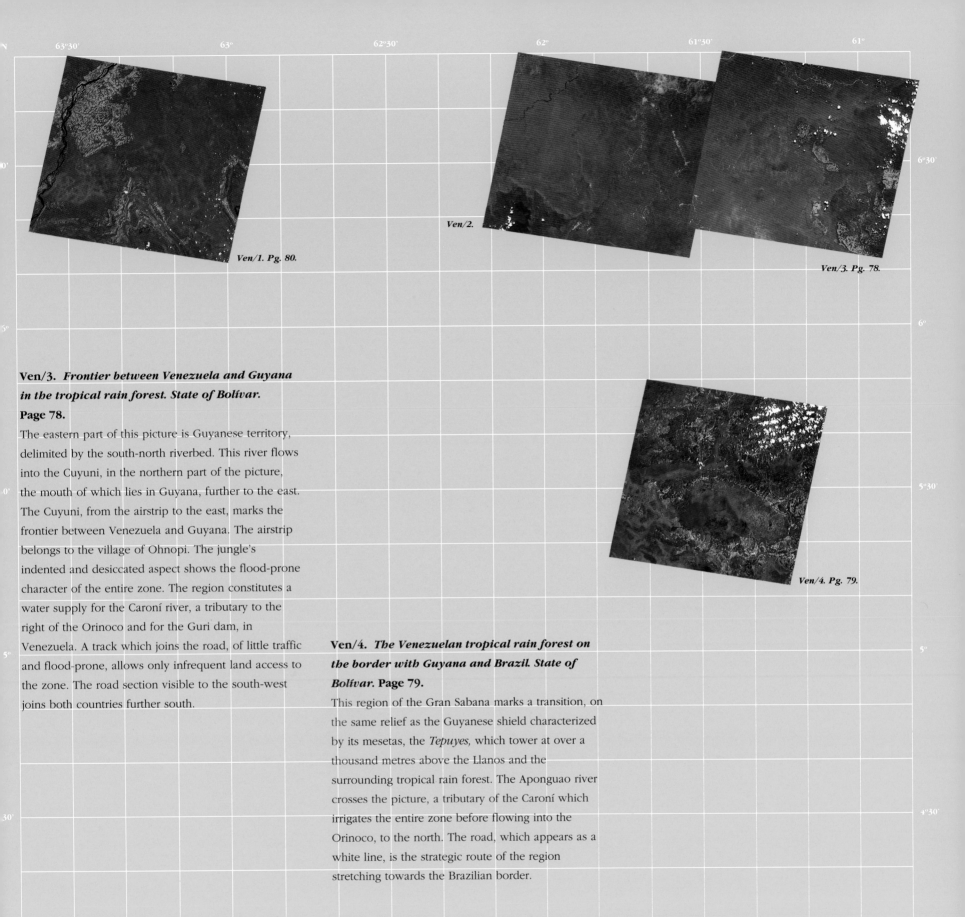

Ven/1. Pg. 80.

Ven/2.

Ven/3. Pg. 78.

Ven/3. *Frontier between Venezuela and Guyana in the tropical rain forest. State of Bolívar.* **Page 78.**

The eastern part of this picture is Guyanese territory, delimited by the south-north riverbed. This river flows into the Cuyuni, in the northern part of the picture, the mouth of which lies in Guyana, further to the east. The Cuyuni, from the airstrip to the east, marks the frontier between Venezuela and Guyana. The airstrip belongs to the village of Ohnopi. The jungle's indented and desiccated aspect shows the flood-prone character of the entire zone. The region constitutes a water supply for the Caroní river, a tributary to the right of the Orinoco and for the Guri dam, in Venezuela. A track which joins the road, of little traffic and flood-prone, allows only infrequent land access to the zone. The road section visible to the south-west joins both countries further south.

Ven/4. Pg. 79.

Ven/4. *The Venezuelan tropical rain forest on the border with Guyana and Brazil. State of Bolívar.* **Page 79.**

This region of the Gran Sabana marks a transition, on the same relief as the Guyanese shield characterized by its mesetas, the *Tepuyes,* which tower at over a thousand metres above the Llanos and the surrounding tropical rain forest. The Aponguao river crosses the picture, a tributary of the Caroní which irrigates the entire zone before flowing into the Orinoco, to the north. The road, which appears as a white line, is the strategic route of the region stretching towards the Brazilian border.

Ven/5. *Flood-prone region on the left bank of the Orinoco, in the state of Anzoátegui, Venezuela.*

The course of the Orinoco can be observed in the south-eastern part of the picture, and one of its tributaries, the Morichal Largo, crosses it like a red streak. The riverside terrain is of little use because flood-prone. The closest fields are devoted to extensive cattle raising. The geometric shapes further away are irrigated ricefields. One notes the existence of foot-shaped fields, the irrigation of which is achieved circularly. This type of irrigation enables the location of circular plots in zones distant from water sources. The rectilinear strip which crosses the large ricefield area corresponds to the power lines coming from Guri and going to Caracas.

Ven/6. *Ciudad Guayana in the state of Delta Amacuro, near the estuary of the Orinoco.* Page 14.

The Caroní river, which flows into the Orinoco, splits Ciudad Guayana in two. The Venezuelan government has decided to transform this zone, only recently developed, into the country's main ricefield. Its flat and flood-prone lands facilitate industrial farming. Effects of this agricultural policy can be perceived on the river's left bank, by the vast geometric fields. Rice monoculture and the steel industry are the zone's resources. As for the city, one observes its recent expansion on the Orinoco's right bank. But it's on the right bank of the Caroní that one notes the highest building density, a mostly industrial sector. Finally, the absence of a bridge over the Orinoco makes necessary the use of a ferry.

Ven/7. *Ciudad Bolívar on the banks of the Orinoco in Venezuela. State of Bolívar.* Page 83.

Ciudad Bolívar owes its dynamism to the Guri dam, which supplies it with energy, and to the bridge over the river which enables communication with the neighbouring state of Anzoátegui, from which it receives resources. This energy, which exceeds local consumption, has allowed the creation of the aluminium industry, with bauxite mining. The presence of alluvial gold in other rivers, as well as iron, also explains the city's wealth and growth. The Orinoco, a hundred kilometres from its estuary, follows a sluggish and broad course, full of sandy islands. The modern city, stretching preferentially on the Orinoco's right bank, fails to enjoy an organized development pattern, whereas the old *barrios* lie along the river because of their ancient port function. The geometric plots, in the city's outskirts, are extensive cattle fields. Road and power line systems trace, to the south, rectilinear corridors on terrains unused because of poor agricultural potential and threat of floods.

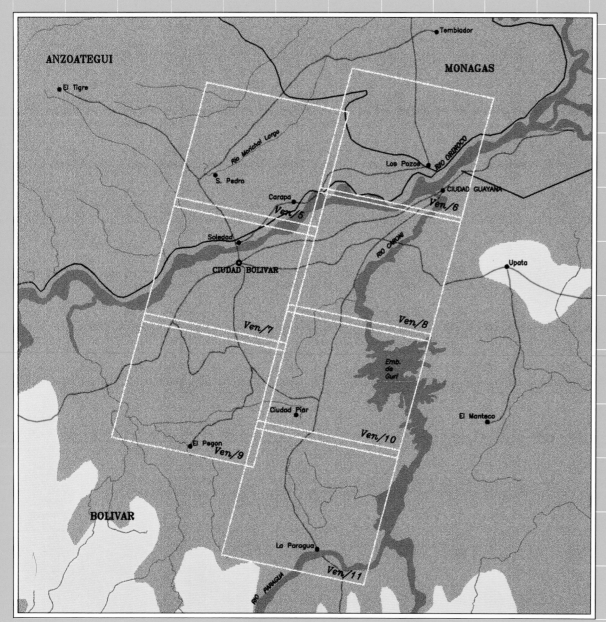

Map 3

Ven/8. *The Caroní flowing into the Orinoco near Ciudad Guayana in Venezuela's tropical rain forest.* **Page 82.**

To the south of the picture one observes the Guri dam and the perimeter of Ciudad Guayana, on the Orinoco to the north. Starting from the Guri dam, recognizable by its grey walls along the reservoir, to the south, the Caroní river appears, with a very wide course indicating brusque variances of volume, which flows further down into the Orinoco, near Ciudad Guayana. One sees the city's suburbs and the immense course of the Orinoco to the north. A road system leaves Ciudad Guayana southwards and passes by Guri. One notes that the urban area is limited to the contours of Ciudad Guayana and, in scarce fashion, to the road. The city consumes Guri's electricity, yet doesn't stretch to the south, but rather along the Orinoco or towards the neighbouring state of Anzoátegui, to the north, where there are oilfields.

Ven/9. *Tropical rain forest zone of Venezuela.*

In the state of Bolívar, south of the Guri dam, west of the Paragua river, lies the transition zone with the *Tepuyes,* mesetas of the Guyanese shield, a piece of the pre-Cambrian base, located furher south. In this region of swamps and jungles, the hydrographic system resembles blood vessels feeding an ubiquitous vegetation. The shades of colour indicate the presence of water and chlorophyllic vegetation. Human presence is limited to sparse narrow roads and burnt, short-lived clearings.

Ven/10. *Guri dam reservoir, on the Caroní river, in the state of Bolívar near Ciudad Bolívar's urban perimeter and the Orinoco.*

The reservoir, the waters of which appear black, makes the region flood-prone. Tall jungle-type vegetation subsists here. One observes the Guri dam in the northern part of the picture, with a nearby airstrip and marks of deforestation around. A road, which runs along the reservoir's west shore, reaches the small town of Ciudad Piar, in the western part of the picture.

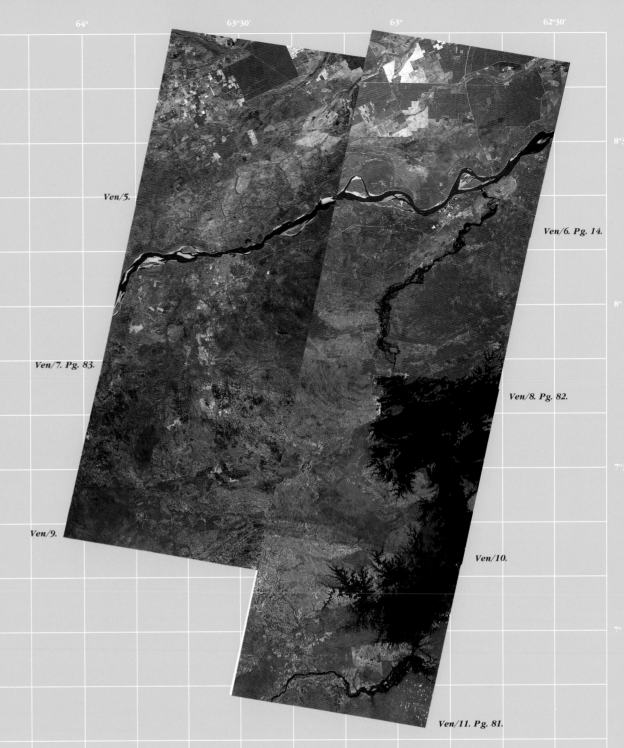

Ven/11. *Confluence of the Paragua and Caroní rivers, at the level of the Guri dam in Venezuelan territory. State of Bolívar.* **Page 81.**

The Paragua river flows into the Caroní, both filling the Guri dam reservoir. The Paragua comes from the west and its junction with the Caroní, of which it is the main tributary, occurs within a delta delimited, to the north, by a "bottleneck". The vast reservoir, known as Guri, makes the zone a natural water supply but also subjects it to high flood risks. One verifies this by the semblance of blood vessels shown by all the ramifications of the hydrographic system. The small town of La Paragua was established on the only ford of its namesake river. One notes an airstrip and the road to Canaima, further south. On the Paragua's left bank, one perceives the characteristic criss-cross pattern of fields dedicated to cattle raising and vegetable farming. This zone is less flood-prone thanks to the local forest, of red colour, which is being gradually burnt down by man.

Ven/12. *Arid region of the Venezuelan Llanos and Playa de Piedra reservoir. State of Guárico. Page 88.*

This area marks the transition between the humid and flood-prone zones from the south inland and the inhabited coast. It is dry, of little activity, and contains the Playa de Piedra reservoir. The zones in white or yellow attest to this dryness. The lakes or reservoirs are not surrounded by signs of strong chlorophyllic activity. The picture's dark-green hue means scarce vegetation. The small town of Tucupido lies on an important inland road system. Its relative isolation, in a zone of little activity, makes it a stopover.

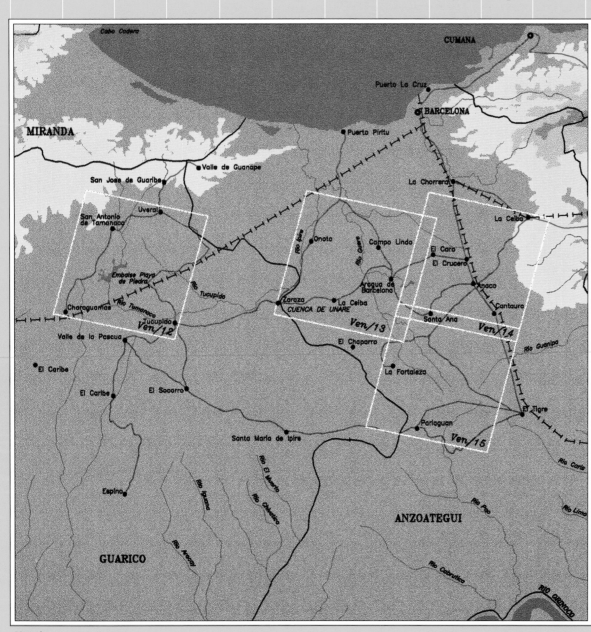

Map 4

Ven/13. *Central Venezuelan Llanos in the state of Anzoátegui.*

This is an oilfield and cattle raising zone. One notes the presence of an important reservoir, on the eastern side of the picture, near the town of Aragua de Barcelona. Two important rivers cross the picture in a south-north direction. The first, the Güere, is fed by the aforementioned reservoir and is a tributary of the second, the Ipire, which flows into the sea. On the latter's left bank, one notes the edge of the Unare basin, near the town of Zaraza. Oil prospecting is an important activity in the region, and the few fields in the picture also reveal intensive cattle raising. This zone lies in an area of transition between the Orinoco, with its energy and farming potential, and the coast where most of the country's population is concentrated.

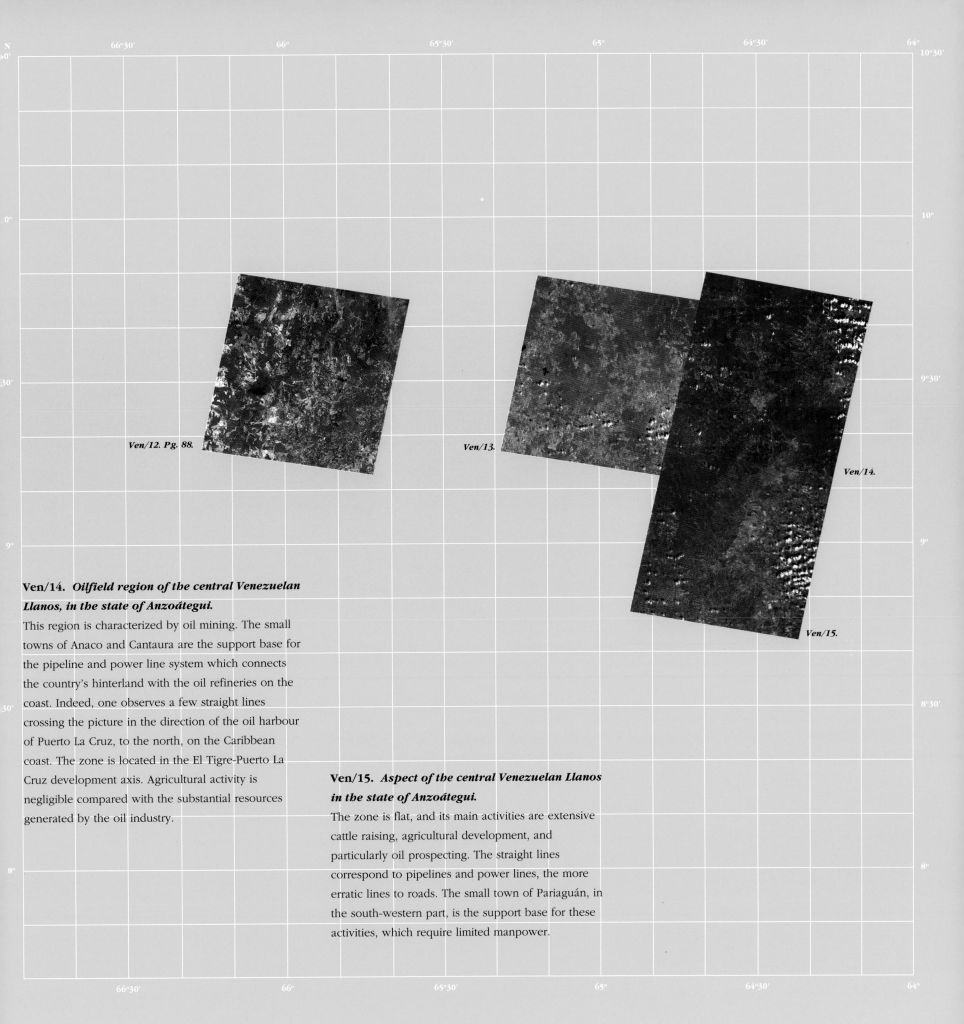

Ven/12. Pg. 88.

Ven/13.

Ven/14.

Ven/15.

Ven/14. *Oilfield region of the central Venezuelan Llanos, in the state of Anzoátegui.*

This region is characterized by oil mining. The small towns of Anaco and Cantaura are the support base for the pipeline and power line system which connects the country's hinterland with the oil refineries on the coast. Indeed, one observes a few straight lines crossing the picture in the direction of the oil harbour of Puerto La Cruz, to the north, on the Caribbean coast. The zone is located in the El Tigre-Puerto La Cruz development axis. Agricultural activity is negligible compared with the substantial resources generated by the oil industry.

Ven/15. *Aspect of the central Venezuelan Llanos in the state of Anzoátegui.*

The zone is flat, and its main activities are extensive cattle raising, agricultural development, and particularly oil prospecting. The straight lines correspond to pipelines and power lines, the more erratic lines to roads. The small town of Pariaguán, in the south-western part, is the support base for these activities, which require limited manpower.

Ven/16. *Eastern shore of Lake Maracaibo and town of Ciudad Ojeda in Venezuela. State of Zulia.* **Page 86.**

One notes the zone's oil industry vocation by the abundance of tanks and pumps on the coast and its proximities. The oilfields are located on the lake's waters and shores, where moles allow access to tankers. On the waters of the lake one observes numerous specks corresponding to wells and passing ships. The mouths of rivers look like white smoke close to the shore. The population nucleus is concentrated on the lake's shore, whereas the inlands are dedicated to subsistence crops. Beginning from the small inner lake located to the east, the cordillera foothills are only sparsely inhabited.

Map 5

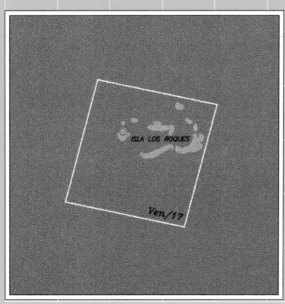

Map 6

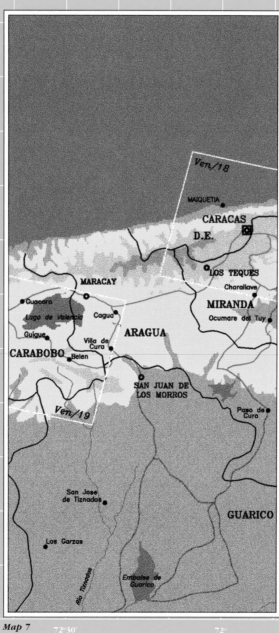

Map 7

Ven/17. *Los Roques coral archipelago, in Venezuela's Caribbean.* **Page 85.**

At the latitude of Maiquetía and Caracas, on the coastline belonging to the Venezuelan *Zona Económica Exclusiva,* the string of coral islands delimits an inner lagoon of little depth. The red colour shows strong chlorophyllic activity of aquatic or lacustrine vegetation. The yellow colour indicates the presence of sandbanks or islands entirely formed of sand. The blue colour of the sea varies according to depth, pale blue for the lagoon to deep blue for the sea. One fails to note any element revealing permanent or transitory human presence.

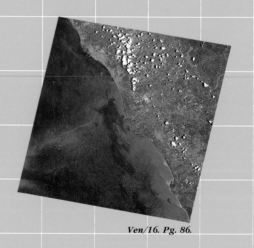

Ven/16. Pg. 86.

Ven/18. *Caracas, the Venezuelan capital, and Maiquetía international airport.* **Page 84.**

The city lies in a depression, 900 m. above sea level. It swoops down towards the coast, and is delimited to the south by the cordillera. Narrowly confined by the depression, the city strives to expand towards Lake Valencia and the Tuy valley to the west, and towards Maiquetía on the coast. The zones of transition towards the coast are classified as natural parks. An extensive motorway system has replaced railways and connects the capital with other urban centres. Tourist activities, beach resorts and the international airport are concentrated in Maiquetía, on the coast. Caracas has moved the oil, chemical and other polluting industries to towns like Los Teques or to the Tuy valley, in the state of Miranda, thus creating industrial centres instead of satellite cities.

Ven/19. *Suburbs of Caracas expanding towards Lake Valencia.* **Page 93.**

In the lower part of the depression, 400 m. above sea level, the city of Caracas spreads under other names. On each side of Lake Valencia lies a satellite town of a half-million people. To the west, Valencia and to the east, Maracay. Other suburbs such as Guacara or Cagua, with over 100,000 inhabitants, outline an almost unified urban cluster. Around the lake, one distinguishes the red streaks of human communities. To the south, the cordillera delimits one of them. The mechanical, chemical and food-processing industries are concentrated here. Cacao and sugarcane are grown windward in this sector. Puerto Cabello, on the coast, is the trading centre for these activities, and a concentration of refineries. The red line appearing on the lake is most probably a sign of pollution.

Ven/17. Pg. 85.

Ven/18. Pg. 84.

Ven/19. Pg. 93.

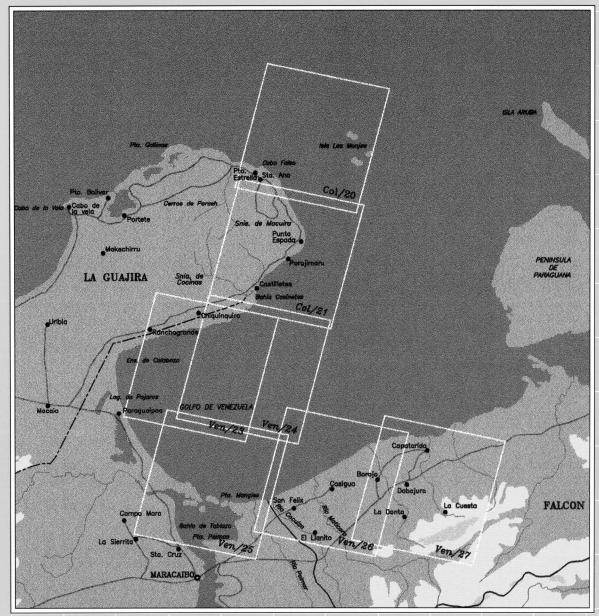

Map 8

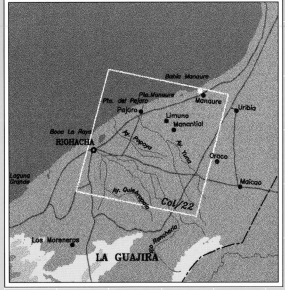

Map 9

Col/21. *Desert zone on Colombia's Caribbean coast. Province of La Guajira.* **Page 91.**

The cape belongs to the west entrance of the Gulf of Venezuela near the border between the two countries. One notes the almost total absence of human activity, except for the straight road lines. One can divide this picture land area in two: the northern part is characterized by a vegetation of small woods on the Serranía de Macuira range, and the southern part by almost total desert, with no signs of plant life. The red patches on the small marine lagoons to the south indicate the presence of littoral woodlands and algæ.

Col/22. *Desert on Colombia's Caribbean coast in the province of La Guajira.*

The almost total absence of the red colour indicating vegetation enhances the river courses, which provide water to the sparse plant life. The irregular red patches enable to situate the few oases of vegetation along their banks. On the coast, sands appear in yellow or white. The absence of mixed colour, which would reveal a terrain of varied crops, also allows to situate the scarce manifestations of human activity. The city of Riohacha appears on the western side of a marine lagoon of grey-coloured waters, due to shallowness and absence of chlorophyllic activity. Road lines are highly visible, and the flat land surface enables right-angle crossroads typical of a desert, level zone. The Manaure salt flats, of a light blue colour, are the only noticeable human activity.

Ven/23. *Aspect of the desert peninsula of La Guajira on the Venezuelan Atlantic coast.*

One observes a road running parallel to the coast: its proximity to the Colombian border confers it strategic interest. At sea one notes the straight furrows of two ships entering the Gulf of Venezuela, probably heading towards Maracaibo harbour. Over the sea's homogeneous blue colour, one can perceive the phenomenon of high-energy particle electron or proton precipitations, which irradiate from Van Allen's Belt surrounding Earth.

Col/20. *Colombian Atlantic coast in the province of La Guajira.*

This part of the coast is the peninsula of La Guajira's easternmost cape on Colombian territory. This peninsula is a desert, which stands out in the picture by its pale or yellow spectral signatures, which correspond to sandy terrain and bare bedrock. Red streaks of vegetation, probably the first slopes of the Serrania de Macuira, show that not all the region is that dry. The white globes, which are low-altitude clouds hovering over the inland peninsula, confirm traces of vegetation by the presence of water evaporation.

Ven/24. *Desert peninsula of La Guajira on the Venezuelan Atlantic coast.*

This zone is located inside the Gulf of Venezuela (also known as Coquibacoa). The picture shows all the spectral signs of bare soils, devoid of vegetation, composed of rock and sand. One observes the eroded course of seasonal rivers, as faults or fissures perpendicular to the coast, parched by the rare passage of waters.

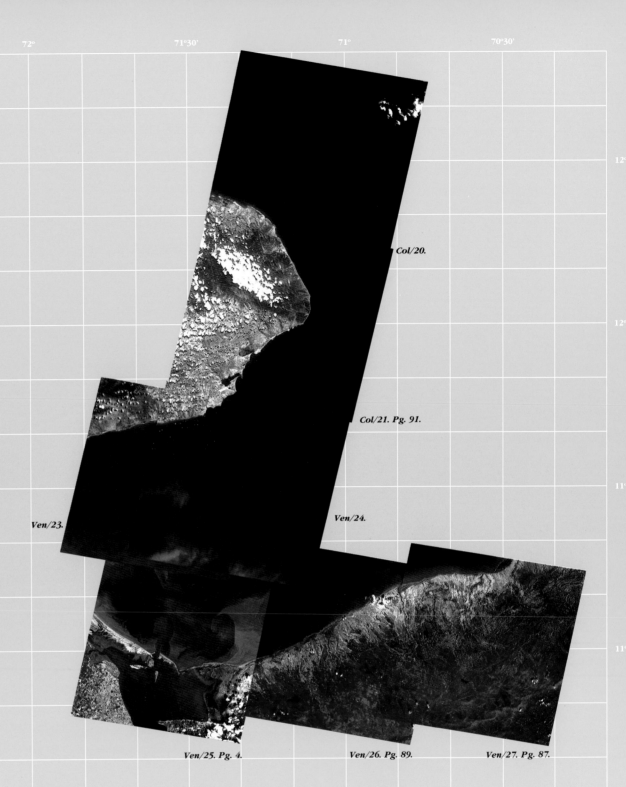

Col/20.

Col/21. Pg. 91.

Ven/23.

Ven/24.

Col/22.

Ven/25. Pg. 4.

Ven/26. Pg. 89.

Ven/27. Pg. 87.

Ven/25. *Bahía del Tablazo and mouth of Lake Maracaibo in the Gulf of Venezuela. State of Zulia.* **Page 4.**

To the north, one observes, in red, the Gulf of Venezuela and the peninsula enclosing Bahía del Tablazo. On the eastern part of the bay lies the complex of refineries which processes oil extracted from Lake Maracaibo. In plain view are many tanks and pipelines reaching the oil terminal and its wharf. On the left shore, to the west of the bay, lies the city of Maracaibo. A dike forms a straight canal at the outlet of Bahía del Tablazo on the Gulf of Venezuela. One can see the wake of a boat leaving the bay, the strong current and the movement of surface waters flowing in and out of it.

Ven/26. *Desert region on Venezuela's Caribbean coast. State of Falcón.* **Page 89.**

This is a transition zone between Caracas and Lake Maracaibo, with the cordillera foothills to the south. One observes two parallel areas in the picture: the sandy, rocky coast in yellow, white and grey, with the flat corridor where communication routes and human activities are concentrated, and above, the cultivations on the irrigated and more fertile part of the cordillera foothills.

Ven/27. *Desert region on the Atlantic coast foothills between the Caracas district and Lake Maracaibo. State of Falcón.* **Page 87.**

One observes the sandy, rocky coast in yellow and white, and the transition to a zone of higher relief revealed by curves. The courses of seasonal rivers are visible, with their meandering and parched aspect. The mountains to the south are the only place where one notes chlorophyllic activity due to rains.

Ven/28. *Aspect of the Venezuelan Llanos in the state of Portuguesa.*

These are zones of savannah, very often featuring taller woodlands along the rivers, with little population. Expansion depends on the irrigation and flooding capacity of dams built in the cordillera. The region lives almost exclusively off cattle raising with processing industries located in the town of Guanare, to the west of the picture, near the Portuguesa river. Fields, mostly devoted to cattle raising, have geometric shapes and colours which vary according to dryness and type of soil. The yellow scar of a pipeline marks the picture to the north-west.

Ven/29. *Contrasts in use of soil in the Venezuelan Llanos. State of Barinas.* **Page 92.**

The picture displays two highly different zones. The northern part is composed of cattle fields, of rectilinear outlines perpendicular to the road. Meat production from this zone, irrigated by dams on the cordillera foothills, constitutes the source of wealth for towns of the foothill plains like Guanare, Barinas and San Fernando, which have food-processing industries. The southern part, delimited by the Portuguesa river, flowing in west-east direction, is formed by unexploited, flood-prone savannah bushlands.

Ven/30. *Transition zone between the eastern foothills of the Cordillera de Mérida and the Llanos. State of Barinas.* **Page 95.**

The towns of Barinas, to the west, and Barrancas further north, profit from their location at a crossroads between different regions. This zone enjoys the benefits of oil from Lake Maracaibo, produce from small farms in the cordillera and trade with the neighbouring Colombian border. It is also a gateway to the Llanos and their cattle raising activities. Thus, Barinas plays an important role in oil prospecting, processing of agricultural produce from the Llanos and interchange between the two countries.

Ven/31. *Savannah in the state of Barinas, in the Venezuelan Llanos.*

One notices the presence of tall woodlands along the rivers flowing from the foothills to irrigate the vast savannah. This is a largely uninhabited zone, devoted exclusively to cattle raising, the products of which are sent to processing plants in towns on the foothills. The landscape is monotonous: endless flood-prone plains, with the straight lines of roads and power lines. The region has been recently opened to settlement.

Ven/32. *Tributaries of the Apure river in the Venezuelan Llanos region. State of Barinas.* **Page 90.**

The region is densely irrigated by tributaries of the Apure river, which springs further south, in the Cordillera de Mérida. Guanarito, on the banks of this river, is a stopover town and support base for local colonization. It is also a gathering point for cattle from the surroundings of the Cordillera de Mérida foothill towns. The monotony of the landscape is due to the flat cattle fields, the low savannah vegetation and the straight road lines. Population density in these territories is negligible, and usually concentrated close to the rivers, on the banks of which one observes woodlands.

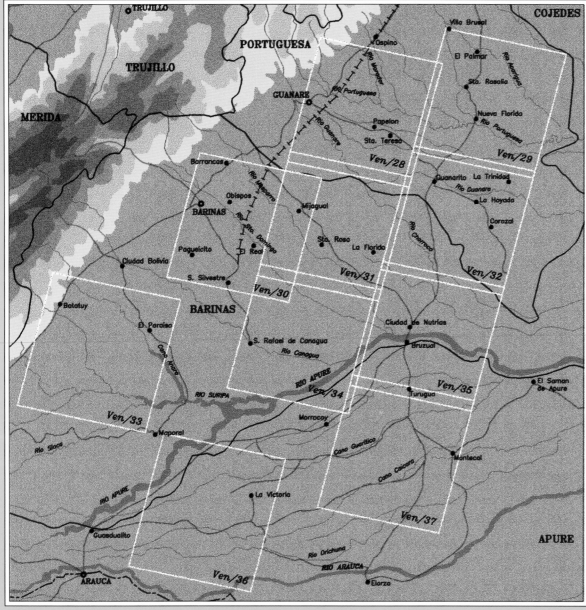

Map 10

Ven/33. *Eastern foothills of the Cordillera de Mérida and beginning of the Llanos. State of Mérida.* **Page 94.**

In the north-western part, one notes mountain foothills, and elsewhere in the picture, plains. These cordillera foothills have been settled for a long time, and the fields' criss-cross pattern reveals intensive small-scale farming. The Caño Anaro river springs in the cordillera, slightly north of the small town of Batatuy, leaning against the mountain. The proximity of Lake Maracaibo facilitates the outflow of the region's farm and oil production. The zone marks the transition between the agricultural Andean foothills and the oil-rich Lake Maracaibo area.

Ven/28.

Ven/29. Pg. 92.

Ven/30. Pg. 95.

Ven/31.
Ven/32. Pg. 90.

Ven/33. Pg. 94.

Ven/34. Pg. 97.

Ven/35. Pg. 41

Ven/37.

Ven/36. Pg. 96.

Ven/34. *Apure river and its tributaries in the Venezuelan Llanos. State of Apure.* **Page 97.**

The Apure river is fed, on its left bank, by tributaries flowing down from the Cordillera de Mérida, which irrigate the plains and flood them in various stretches. The systematic use of airstrips, and its marks on the landscape, emphasizes the changes in farming trends and the remoteness of organized human centres.

Ven/35. *Course of the Apure river in the Venezuelan Llanos. State of Apure.* **Page 41.**

The Apure river marks a threshold in settlement of the region. The small town of Nutrias, located on the ford of the Apure, with the airstrip of Bruzual on the right bank, is the only communication link with the human concentrations far to the west in the Cordillera de Mérida. The roads crossing the river contribute to recent colonization towards the south-west.

Ven/36. *The Venezuelan Llanos near the frontier with Colombia. State of Táchira.* **Page 96.**

One observes the Arauca river in the south-eastern part of the picture. This is a region of savannah shrublands, of a green colour, only recently settled and sparsely inhabited. Relative road density indicates a zone of traffic in the proximity of the Colombian frontier.

Ven/37. *Aspect of the Venezuelan Llanos, between the Apure and Arauca rivers.*

One observes the Guaritico river crossing the picture from west to east, and the colonization road north-south. Even the tiniest town has an airstrip, such as Turugua on the Guaritico and Mantecal on the Caicara, further south. The smaller road follows the course of the Guaritico, while the main road leads to the Arauca river.

Col/38. *City of Barranquilla on Colombia's Caribbean coast. Province of Atlántico.* Page 98.

One observes the city of Barranquilla and the estuary of the Magdalena river. The cone of the estuary is very large, around ten kilometres-wide at sea, due to the river's enormous volume. The river's abundance in organic waste is well-known, and increases in the rainy season, the strong sea current thrusting it westward. Along the river, the red spectral signature indicates high chlorophyllic activity, due to the presence of mangrove swamp-type aquatic plant life. On the other hand, fields on the left bank are of a green colour, which reveals cattle raising activity or areas of scant irrigation.

Col/39. *Cities of Ciénaga and Santa Marta, on Colombia's Caribbean coast. Province of Magdalena.* Page 99.

Two natural systems appear clearly: on the unclouded coast, the Ciénaga Grande swamplands with the cities of Ciénaga and Santa Marta, and the mountainous area covered in clouds of the Sierra Nevada de Santa Marta. The Ciénaga Grande is characterized by sea water infiltration and the *Troncal del Caribe* motorway, which runs along the coastal strip between swamp and sea. The motorway passes through Pueblo Viejo and Ciénaga, and continues north towards Santa Marta. The grey colour indicates a desert-like environment formed by littoral woodlands petrified by saltwater.

Col/40. *Bay of Cartagena, and the city of Cartagena de Indias. Province of Bolívar.* Page 103.

The city stands out in the picture by the grey-white colour of buildings. One observes the bay with the straits of Bocachica and Bocagrande, side by side. The red ochre blot is La Popa hill, with the monastery of the same name at the top. Nearby, the small white spot corresponds to the castle of San Felipe. One discerns the mouth of the Canal del Dique, which reaches the Bay of Cartagena at its southern extremity, and refuse matter in the bay's waters, showing as a greyish stain.

Col/41. *Swamps bordering the Magdalena river between the provinces of Bolívar and Magdalena, in Colombia.* Page 100.

One identifies the flood-prone zones by their proximity to the Magdalena river, which crosses the picture in south-north direction, within the geographic system known as the Mompox depression, and by the intense red of aquatic vegetation around the swamps. One observes the grey straight line of the Canal del Dique, which flows out of the Magdalena near the small town of Calamar. To the north, one distinguishes the small towns of Campo de la Cruz, on the river's left bank, Salamina, on the right bank, and Remolino, in the north of the picture. Cultivated zones appear in pale, ochre or yellow, and zones of virgin aquatic or woodland vegetation in redder shades.

Col/42. *Plains on the Colombian Caribbean and Sierra Nevada de Santa Marta. Province of Magdalena.* Page 101.

This is a transition zone between the swamps to the north-west, the first outcrops of the Sierra Nevada de Santa Marta and the extensive cattle fields to the south. Waters, with rectilinear shores on the north-western edge of the picture, belong to the Ciénaga Grande swamplands, characterized by a chlorophyll-active aquatic vegetation. It is delimited, to the south, by the road which links, from west to east, the small towns of Pivijay, Media Luna, Fundación and Aracataca. Further along, the road extends to Ciénaga, to the north, passing through zones of irrigated fields appearing in red. To the east begins the Sierra Nevada de Santa Marta.

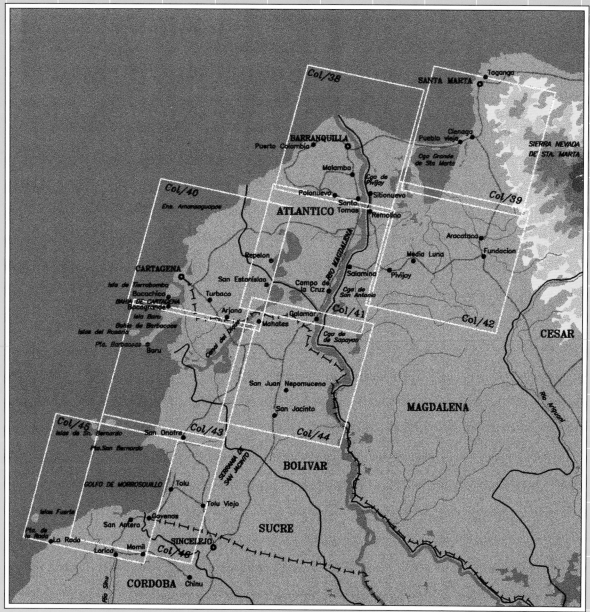

Map 11

Col/43. *Barú island and Bahía de Barbacoas on Colombia's Caribbean coast. Province of Bolívar.* **Page 22.**

One can observe the island of Barú, forming the Bahía de Barbacoas, and, to the west, the Rosario islands, with their coral reefs. The island to the south of the picture is the main island of the San Bernardo archipelago. The red central area corresponds to aquatic vegetation growing at the mouth of various swamps fed by the waters of the Magdalena river.

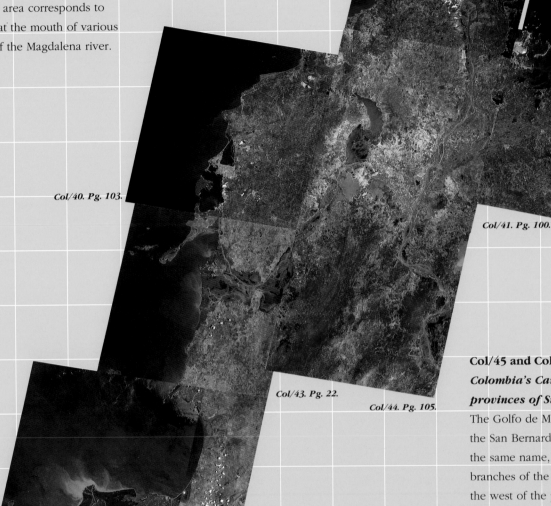

Col/38. Pg. 98.

Col/39. Pg. 99.

Col/40. Pg. 103.

Col/41. Pg. 100.

Col/42. Pg. 101.

Col/43. Pg. 22.

Col/44. Pg. 105.

Col/45. Pg. 104.

Col/46. Pg. 102.

Col/45 and Col/46. *Golfo de Morrosquillo on Colombia's Caribbean coast between the provinces of Sucre and Córdoba.* **Page 104.**

The Golfo de Morrosquillo is delimited to the north by the San Bernardo point, to the west by the islands of the same name, and to the south by the three branches of the Sinú river estuary. The large island, to the west of the picture, is Isla Fuerte, facing Punta de la Rada. Outside the Sinú delta mangrove swamps, of high chlorophyllic activity appearing in bright red, the vegetation is of ochre colour. Human activity manifests itself with straight road lines, the small towns of San Antero, on the west side of a pronounced meander of the Sinú, and Lorica, to the south of the picture. The village of Momil, east of Lorica and close to the north shore of the Ciénaga Grande swamplands, can be distinguished by its grey colour. The naval base of Coveñas, with its aerodrome, where the pipeline coming from the Caño Limón oilfields ends, appears on the gulf's south-eastern side. The shallowness of waters around the San Bernardo islands and their coral girdle is shown by a shade paler than the deep hue of the high sea.

Col/44. *The Mompox depression between the provinces of Bolívar and Magdalena, in Colombia.* **Page 105.**

In this zone, the Magdalena river reaches its estuary. The large swamp is called Sapayán, and others in the north-western part are crossed by the Canal del Dique before arriving in Cartagena. A series of small hills in south-north direction crosses the picture, demarcating the two swamp systems and causing a bend in the canal. The small towns of Nepomuceno and San Jacinto appear at the centre of the picture, Mahates on the banks of the canal, and Calamar to the north, on the Magdalena, where the canal originates.

Pan/47. *Gulf of Panama, Panama City and Pacific entrance to the Canal.* Page 109.

On the left side of Panama City, one clearly sees the entrance to the Canal, with a dike which prolongs it to the Gulf of Panama and Taboga islands. The man-excavated stretch continues on to the lakes of Gatún to the west and Madden to the east. Opened in 1914, under United States administration, the Panama Canal will be returned to the Panamanian nation in 1999. The main users are the United States and Japan. Nearly half the country's population is concentrated in Panama City, over 800,000 people. The city has four airports and devotes itself almost exclusively to financial activities, as a Free Zone. The coast, near the small town of Arraijan, west of the Canal, is characterized by extensive cattle raising and subsistence agriculture, mainly rice and sugarcane, whereas large multinational companies grow bananas and other fruits. On the gulf and along the Canal, one can see several dots or little streaks, which are ships sailing from one ocean to the other.

Pan/47. Pg. 109.

Pan/48.

Pan/49. Pg. 108.

Pan/48. *Bay of Panama east of Panama City and the Canal entrance.*

In the gulf's environs one observes the Otoque islands, and on the coastal inland mangrove swamps. A few aquatic cultivations, probably shrimp farming, spread out close to the gulf, shaped like irrigated fields with regular lines. Further inland, one notes the small black streak of the Chame airstrip near the coastal village of Playa Coronado.

Pan/49. *Peninsula of Azuero and Golfo de Montijo in southern Panama.* Page 108.

This zone is characterized by coffee plantations in the high valleys, and cattle raising on their drier slopes. In the picture, one notes the deep red of the coastal mangrove swamps and the estuary of the San Pablo river. In the inner valley, the banks of the Santa María river have a relatively dense population. Inhabitants of the Azuero peninsula live off a food industry based on citrus fruits, sugarcane, rice and tomatoes.

Map 12

Col/50. *Golfo de Urabá on Colombia's Caribbean coast, in the provinces of Antioquia and Chocó.* Page 107.

In the picture, the biggest river is the Atrato, the south-north course of which ends in a marshy delta on the Golfo de Urabá. Because the river drains off a considerable tropical jungle territory, its alluvial cone spews forth an abundance of organic matter, which forms a distinct smudge in the gulf. The dominant shade in the picture is red, due to the vegetation's high chlorophyllic activity. This region is one of the rainiest in the world, with a yearly precipitation of over ten metres, due to its geographic situation in the zone of intertropical convergence. The sharpness of the picture enables one to observe the general movement of the waters, which, during this season, are driven by a prevailing north-to-east wind. Human presence is represented, to the east, by the town of Turbo, characterized by the chessboard pattern of its streets, shown in grey. To the west of the gulf, one observes, with greater difficulty, the tiny towns of Unguía and Santa María, originally known as Santa María del Darién, the first Spanish settlement in America. The harbour was abandoned due to sanding-up of the gulf.

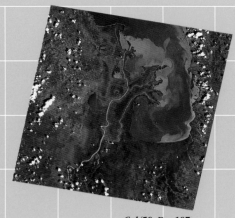

Col/50. Pg. 107.

Col/51. Pg. 106.

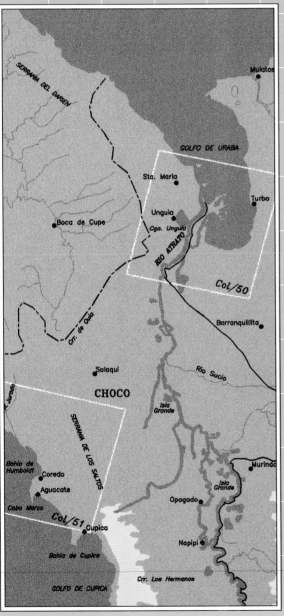

Map 13

Col/51. *The Colombian Pacific coast near the frontier with Panama. Province of Chocó.* Page 106.

The region is almost entirely tropical rain forest. One observes Cabo Marzo, with the villages of Aguacate to the south and Coredo to the north, on the Bay of Humboldt, and the Serranía de los Saltos, with mangrove swamps by the sea. The latter are identified by an intense red hue, indicating high chlorophyllic activity. The border zone with Panama begins a few kilometres further north with the Cordillera de Juradó and the Darién Gap. The estuary of the river, which flows parallel to the coast, shows with a clear colour, as it disgorges fluvial matter on the dark sea bottom. From the human aspect, the zone is practically uninhabited, except the two aforementioned villages, which have airstrips, although too small to be seen. Clouds appear by groups in linear formations more or less perpendicular to the coast, and are always concentrated over land, where evaporation is stronger than over the sea.

Col/52. *Mountainous region of Colombia's Cordillera Central in the provinces of Caldas and Antioquia.* Page 110.

The main river, in the centre of the picture, is the Cauca. Its northern tributary, on the right bank, is the Arma, which flows east to west along a very confined course. The southern tributary, also on the right bank, is the Pozo. One can observe that the Cauca flows more or less parallel to the cordillera. Despite their altitude, the original mountain forests have been laid waste by man: only the highest reaches of the cordillera display dark patches. One sees several towns, such as Sonsón, to the north-east of the picture, on a plain propitious to farming activities,

identified by the small red spots; from north to south, Aguadas, Pácora and Salamina, on the right bank of the Cauca river, saddled on smaller mountains. On the left bank appear the towns of Marmato, Supía and Riosucio, relatively close to each other. In this transition zone between the cities of Cali and Medellín, human activity next to the river remains considerable. On the contrary, the south-eastern part of the picture, from pale to yellow, shows the slopes' impressive erosion and aridity.

Col/53. *Cauca river between the Cordillera Central and Occidental in the provinces of Caldas, Quindío, Risaralda and Valle.* Page 111.

One observes the mountainous aspect of the zone by the marked incisions of the terrain, the frequent gorges originating in the Cordillera Central, resembling grey or blue snakes in the picture, and the main rivers, of a less erratic course. The flat area corresponds to the course of the Cauca river, in its southern stretch, while it still belongs to Valle del Cauca province, near the small town of La Virginia. Another important river, the Chinchiná, a tributary of the Cauca, can be seen from its source in the Nevado del Ruiz to its junction with the Cauca, passing through the town of Chinchiná. The two big cities, grey blots on a red background, are Manizales, to the north, capital of Caldas province, and Pereira, further south, capital of Risaralda province. The two intermediate towns are, from north to south, Chinchiná and Santa Rosa de Cabal. The mountain region's major agricultural activity, especially in the Cordillera Central, is coffee, backbone of the development and prosperity of Manizales and Pereira. Other crops, in the orderly and geometric fields of the Cauca and La Virginia valleys, are rice, sugarcane or cotton.

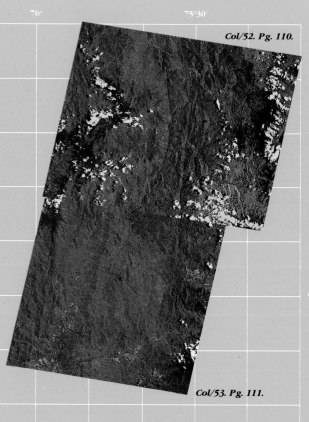

Col/52. Pg. 110.

Col/53. Pg. 111.

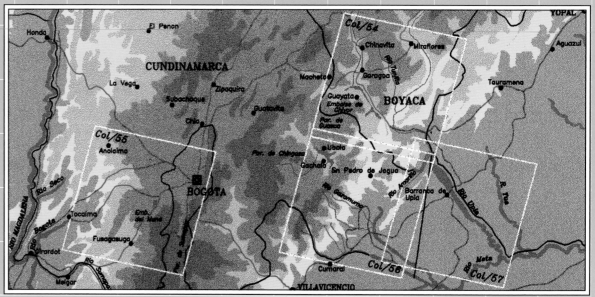

Map 14

Map 15

74

Col/54. *The Colombian Cordillera Oriental in the provinces of Boyacá and Cundinamarca.* **Page 114.**

This zone, with its deep valleys and soaring slopes, serves as a natural reserve for several hydroelectric dams. The dam appearing in the picture is Chivor, with its turbine sector in the lower part. The vegetation is of *páramo* type, and displays a green or dark red spectral signature, which indicates weak chlorophyllic activity, due to altitude. These zones soak up water like a natural sponge, and are the source of various rivers flowing down into the Orinoco. Human presence is denoted by the small towns of Garagoa, to the north of the dam, and Guayatá, to the east, and mainly by the roads crossing the cordillera eastwards.

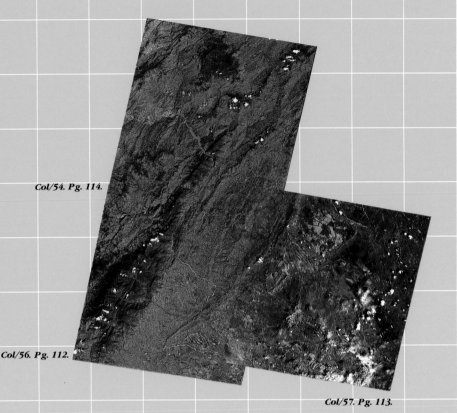

Col/54. Pg. 114.

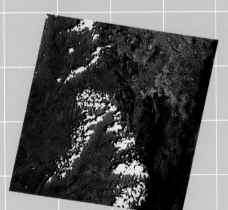

Col/55. Pg. 46.

Col/56. Pg. 112.

Col/57. Pg. 113.

Col/55. *Santa Fe de Bogotá, the Colombian capital, in the Sabana de Bogotá. Province of Cundinamarca.* **Page 46.**

South and downtown Bogotá can be observed, followed by the *páramo* of Sumapaz in the southern part of the picture. One notes the Sabana de Bogotá as it meets the western foothills of the Cordillera Oriental, which plunges down into the Magdalena river. In this part of the foothills, one can observe towns strewn along the main highways, southwards to Girardot and Melgar passing by Fusagasugá, and northwards to Medellín passing by Honda. These towns are situated on mesetas eroded by the Sumapaz and Bogotá rivers, tributaries of the Magdalena. On the Sabana de Bogotá, one clearly discerns chequer fields alternating with the plastic roofs of flower nurseries.

Col/56. *Foothills of the Colombian Cordillera Oriental overlooking the Llanos in the provinces of Cundinamarca and Meta.* **Page 112.**

The mountain area is characterized by the barren aspect of the rugged terrain, with parallel ridge lines, and the dark green colour of mountain vegetation. This zone, on the limits of the *páramos* of Sumapaz, to the south, and Chingaza, to the north, is the fountainhead of the great eastern rivers, owing to its great rainfall. A flat zone of transition, with small villages, appears crossed by several minor rivers, all tributaries of the Meta river. One can distinguish the relatively straight lines of roads and chequer pattern of a few cultivated fields. After a last stretch of the cordillera, in a south-west to north-west orientation, the plains of the Meta open out, with geometric fields devoted to industrial crops.

Col/57. *Region of the Colombian eastern Llanos in the provinces of Meta and Casanare.* **Page 113.**

The Upía river flows down the Cordillera Oriental, in the north-west side of the picture, from Lake Tota in Boyacá to the Meta in the south-east. The course of these rivers is variable, with many islands. In the north-west part of the picture, parallel contour lines indicate a mountainous area, the cordillera's eastern foothills. The village of Barranca de Upía, on the left bank of the Upía, appears clearly at the end of the road. The dark or black spots reveal flood-prone zones. The predominant green colour denotes the presence of grasslands, with a chorophyllic activity distinct from forests, showing in red.

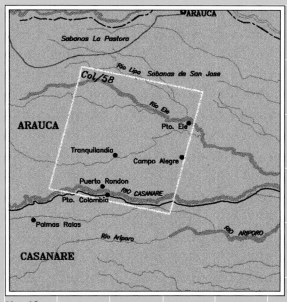

Map 16

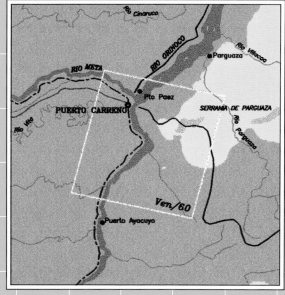

Map 18

Col/58. Pg. 115.

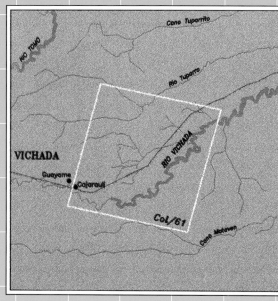

Map 17

Map 19

Col/58. *Region of Colombia's eastern Llanos. Province of Arauca.* Page 115.

This is a transition zone between woodlands along river courses and the Llanos grasslands on the border area between Colombia and Venezuela, in the province of Arauca. The main geographic interest of the picture is to show the multitude of rivers springing in the Cordillera Oriental which are major tributaries of the Casanare, Arauca and Meta. Red and green hues indicate the predominant type of vegetation. Red corresponds to woodlands along the riverbanks, and green to grasslands formed by tall pastures and small trees. Black corresponds to the many lakes which denote the zone's marshy environment. Human presence is apparent with the straight road lines and the airstrip of Pueblo Rondón, on the left bank of the Casanare. The white sandbanks on the river look like islands.

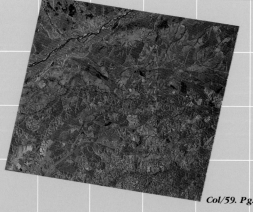

Col/59. Pg. 116.

Col/59. *Region of Colombia's eastern Llanos in the provinces of Meta and Casanare.* **Page 116.**

The big river in the north-western part of the picture is the Meta, with its tributary Cravo Sur. The region's flat aspect is verified by the fluctuating courses of main and secondary rivers, with their many meanders and islands. Erosion, caused by the Muco river and its tributaries in west-east direction, is considerable and forms a whole network of micro-indentations in a garland pattern. Vegetation is concentrated on riverbanks, earning it the name of *bosque galería,* which illustrates its corridor-like aspect. Human presence is negligible, only noticeable by the roads following the hydrographic system. Carimagua, in the centre of the picture, is located near an airtsrip. Organized, geometric clearings, to the right of the Meta, indicates a particular soil usage. The white spots on the meanders of secondary rivers are sandbanks.

Ven/60. *The Meta flowing into the Orinoco, on the border between Colombia and Venezuela.* **Page 26.**

The zone east of the Orinoco, which flows south to north, belongs to Venezuela and marks the beginning of the Serranía de Parguaza tropical rain forest region. The zone west of the Orinoco and south of the Meta belongs to Colombia and is composed of flood-prone savannahs. Each country marks its strategic position with a small town on both sides of the river, with military outposts and an airstrip: Puerto Carreño, on the Colombian side, and Puerto Paéz, on the Venezuelan side. Despite political efforts to encourage colonization, human presence remains scarce, because of difficult living conditions and communications.

Ven/60. Pg. 26.

Col/61. *Llanos and jungle in eastern Colombia near the border with Venezuela. Province of Vichada.* **Page 117.**

The Vichada river meanders across the picture through marshy, flat terrain. It divides two distinct geographic areas. To the south, in red, the dense tropical rain forest of high chlorophyllic activity, practically untouched by man. To the north, a transition zone with a medley of jungle, swamp, labyrinths of dried-out riverbeds and clearings hacked or burnt open by man. One observes a main road, crossing the picture from west to east, which leads to Puerto Nariño on the frontier between Colombia and Venezuela, at the confluence of the Vichada and Orinoco. The most interesting visual detail is the *bosque galería* system along rivers and ravines, which appear strikingly like blood vessels draining the jungle.

Col/61. Pg. 117.

Frontier between Venezuela and Guyana
in the tropical rain forest. State of Bolívar.

Ven/3, page 59

*The Venezuelan tropical rain forest on the border with
Guyana and Brazil. State of Bolívar.*

Ven/4, page 59

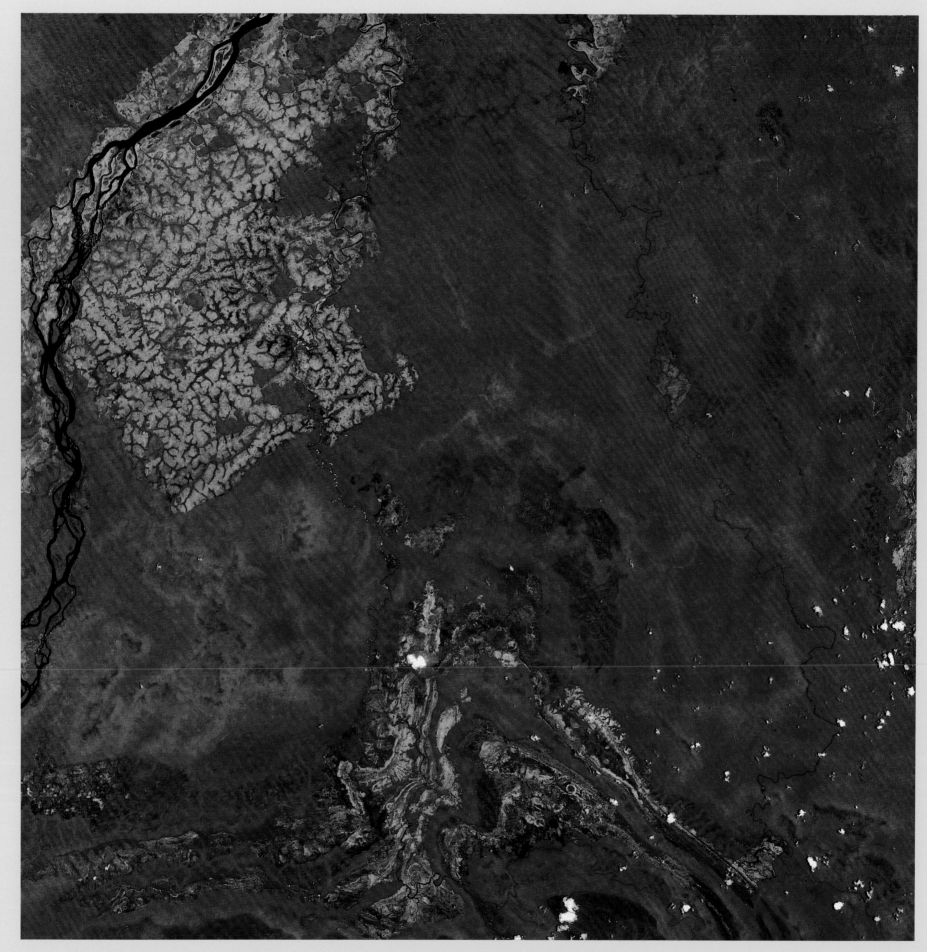

*The Venezuelan tropical rain forest as it merges
into the Tepuyes zone. State of Bolívar.*

Ven/1, page 59

*Confluence of the Paragua and Caroní rivers, at the level of
the Guri dam in Venezuelan territory. State of Bolívar.*

Ven/11, page 61

The Caroní flowing into the Orinoco
near Ciudad Guayana, in Venezuela's tropical rain forest.

Ven/8, page 61

Ciudad Bolívar on the banks of the Orinoco
in Venezuela. State of Bolívar.

Ven/7, page 61

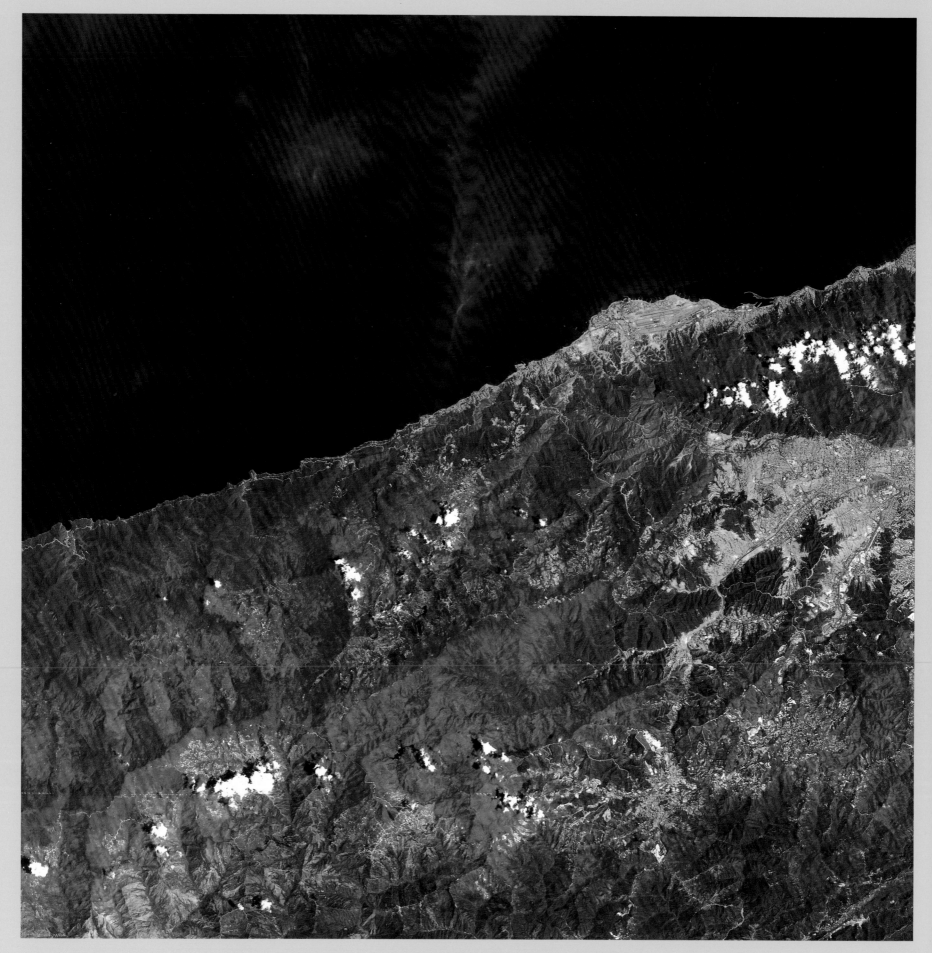

Caracas, the Venezuelan capital,
and Maiquetía international airport.

Ven/18, page 65

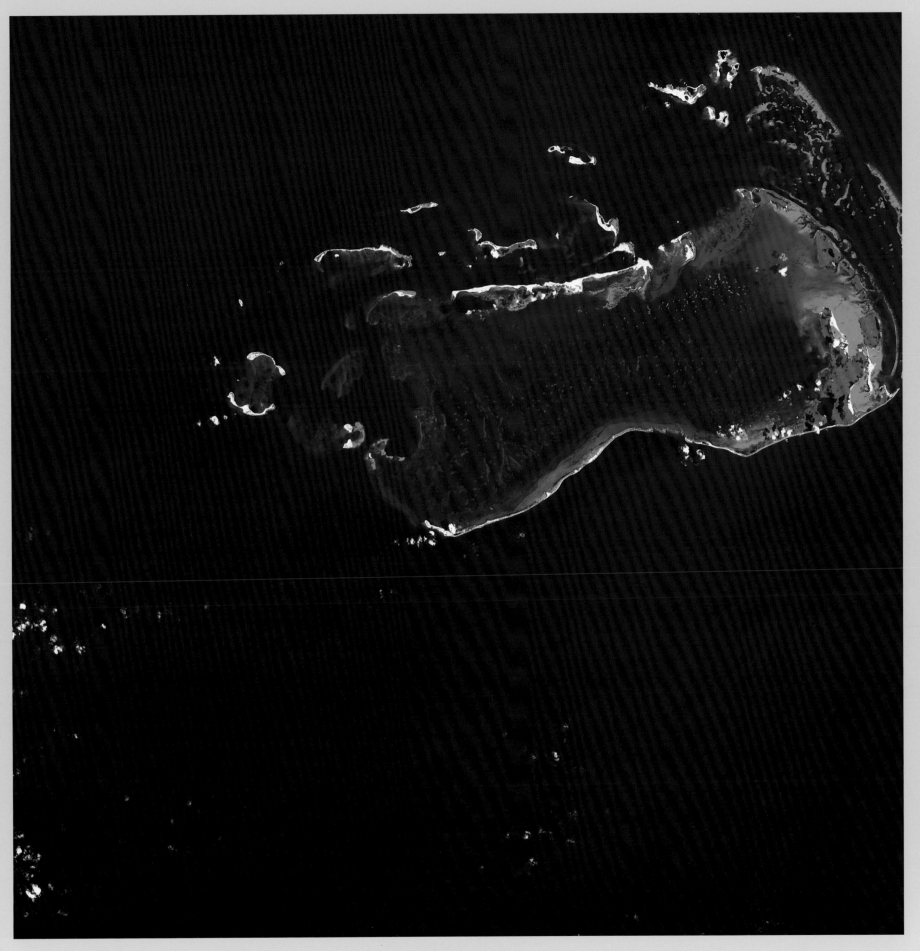

Los Roques coral archipelago,
in Venezuela's Caribbean.

Ven/17, page 65

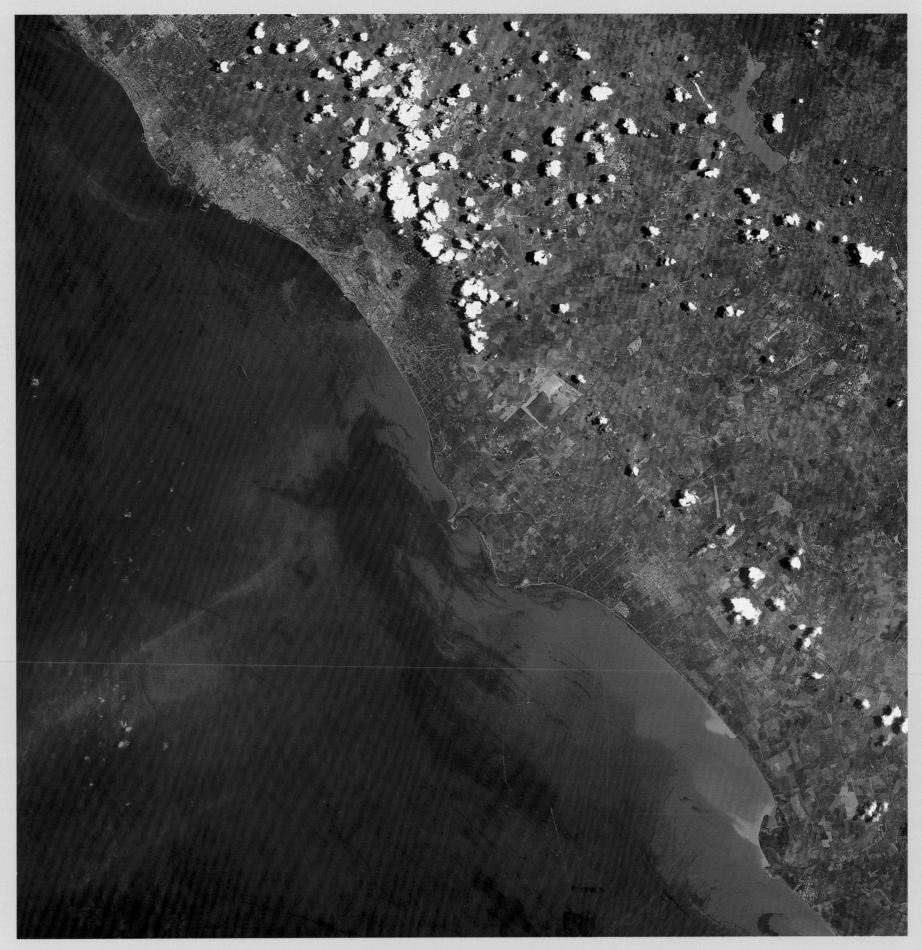

*Eastern shore of Lake Maracaibo
and town of Ciudad Ojeda in Venezuela. State of Zulia.*

Ven/16, page 64

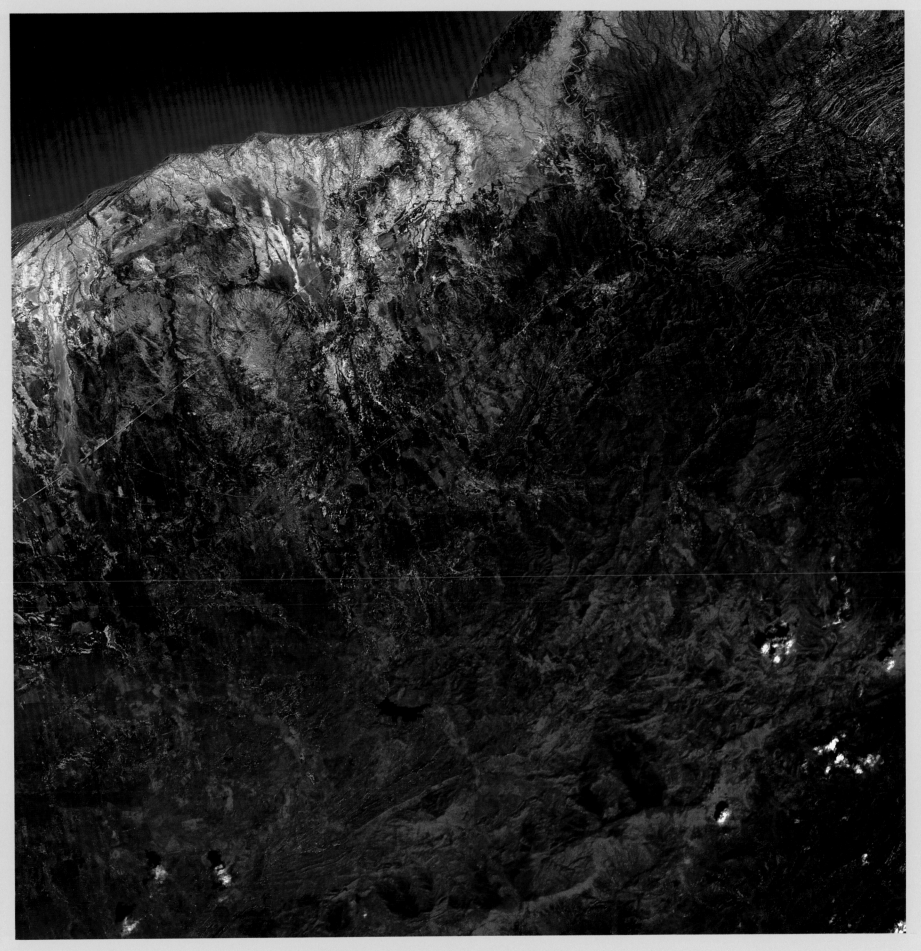

*Desert region on the Atlantic coast foothills between the
Caracas district and Lake Maracaibo. State of Falcón.*

Ven/27, page 67

Arid region of the Venezuelan Llanos
and Playa de Piedra reservoir. State of Guárico.

Ven/12, page 63

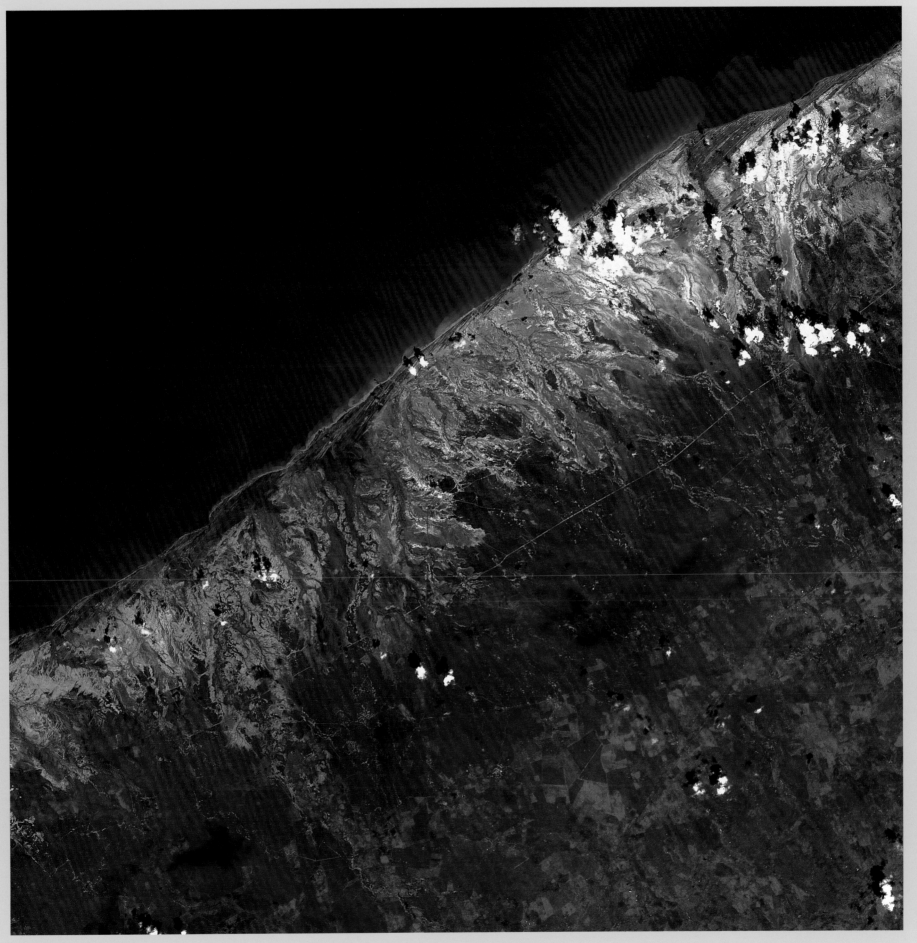

Desert region on Venezuela's Caribbean coast.
State of Falcón.

Ven/26, page 67

*Tributaries of the Apure river
in the Venezuelan Llanos region. State of Barinas.*

Ven/32, page 69

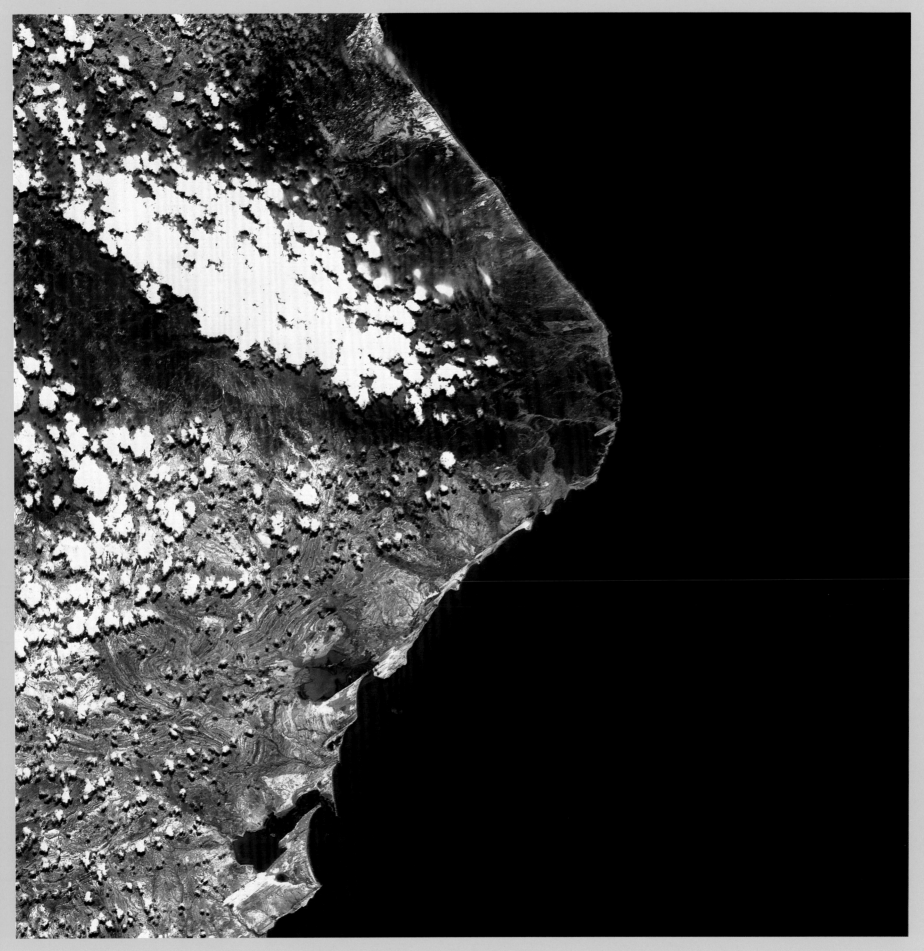

Desert zone on Colombia's Caribbean coast.
Province of La Guajira.

Col/21, page 67

*Contrasts in use of soil
in the Venezuelan Llanos. State of Barinas.*

Ven/29, page 69

Suburbs of Caracas
expanding towards Lake Valencia.

Ven/19, page 65

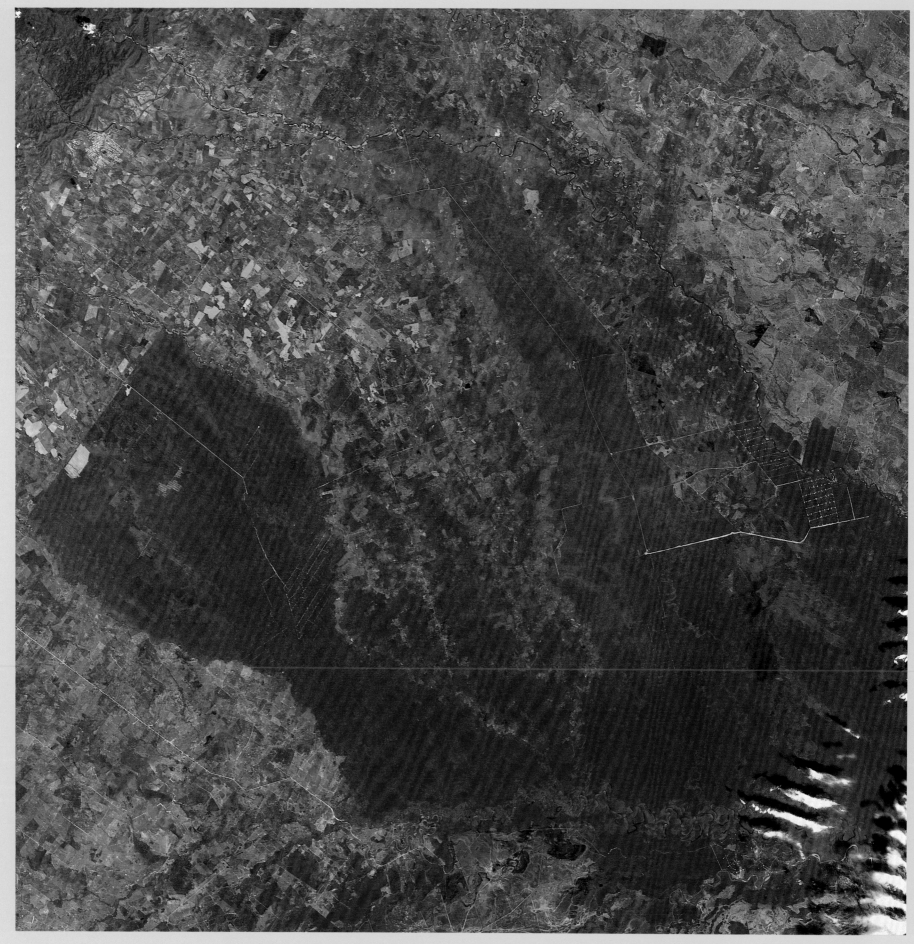

*Eastern foothills of the Cordillera de Mérida
and beginning of the Llanos. State of Mérida.*

Ven/33, page 69

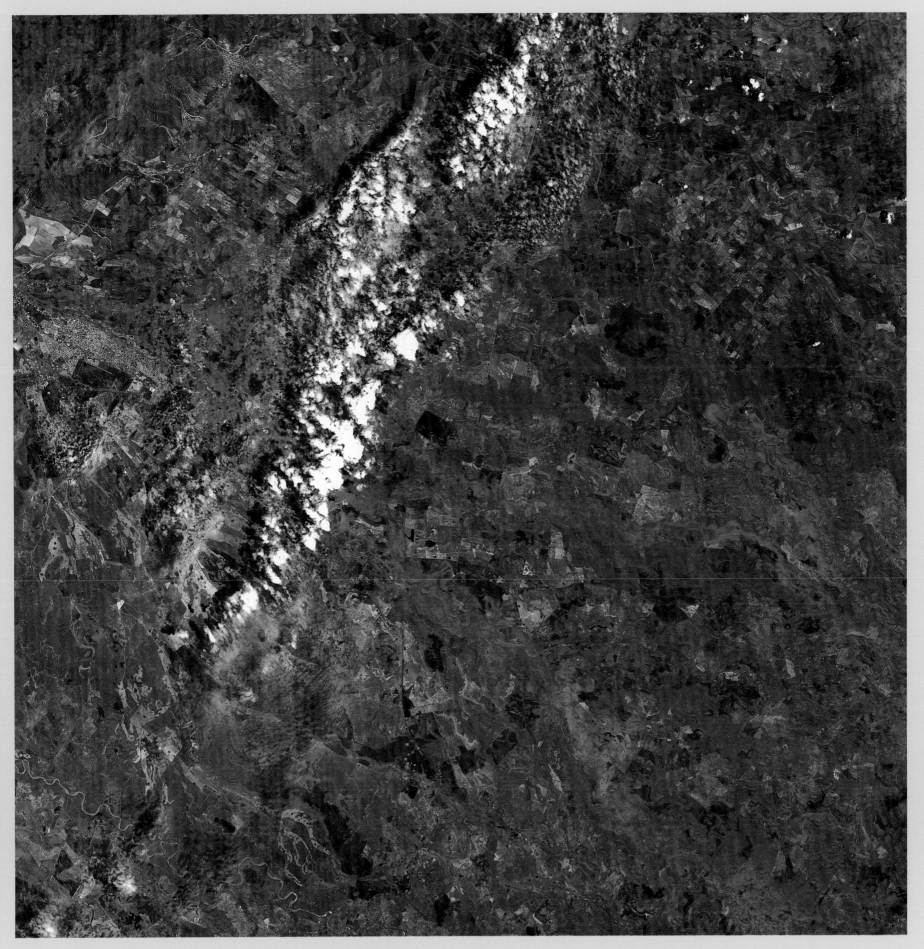

*Transition zone between the eastern foothills
of the Cordillera de Mérida and the Llanos. State of Barinas.*

Ven/30, page 69

The Venezuelan Llanos
near the frontier with Colombia. State of Táchira.

Ven/36, page 69

*Apure river and its tributaries
in the Venezuelan Llanos. State of Apure.*

Ven/34, page 69

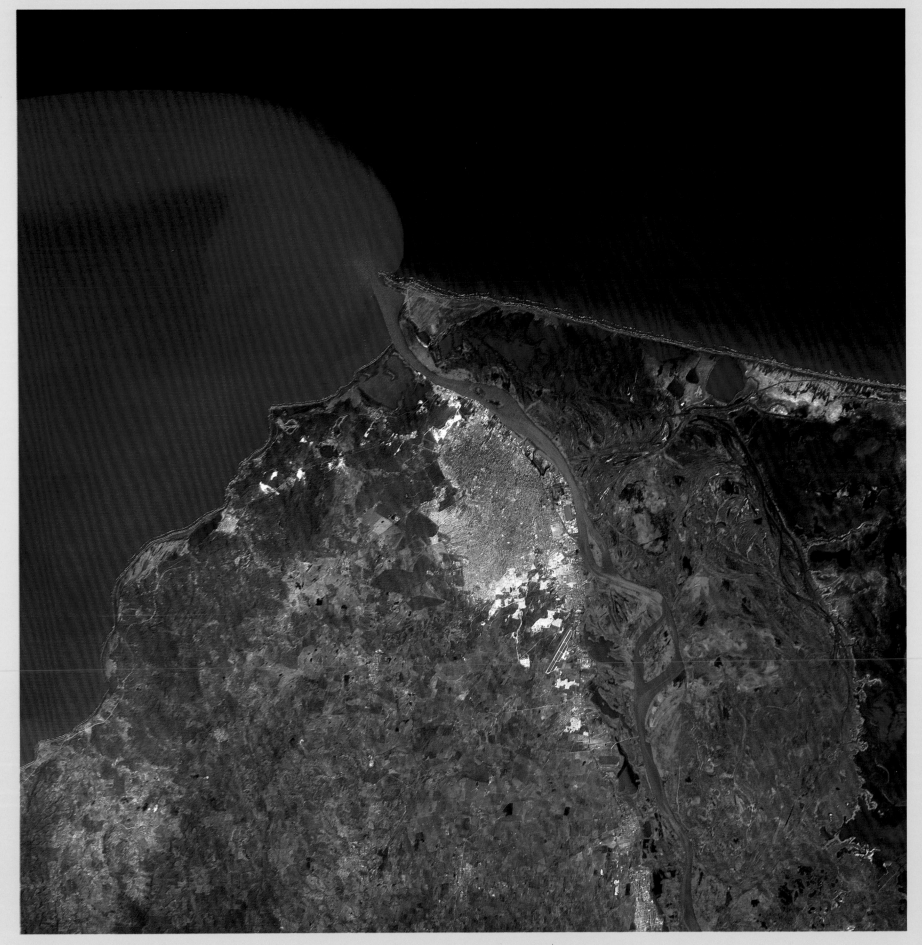

City of Barranquilla on Colombia's Caribbean coast.
Province of Atlántico.

Col/38, page 71

Cities of Ciénaga and Santa Marta,
on Colombia's Caribbean coast. Province of Magdalena.

Col/39, page 71

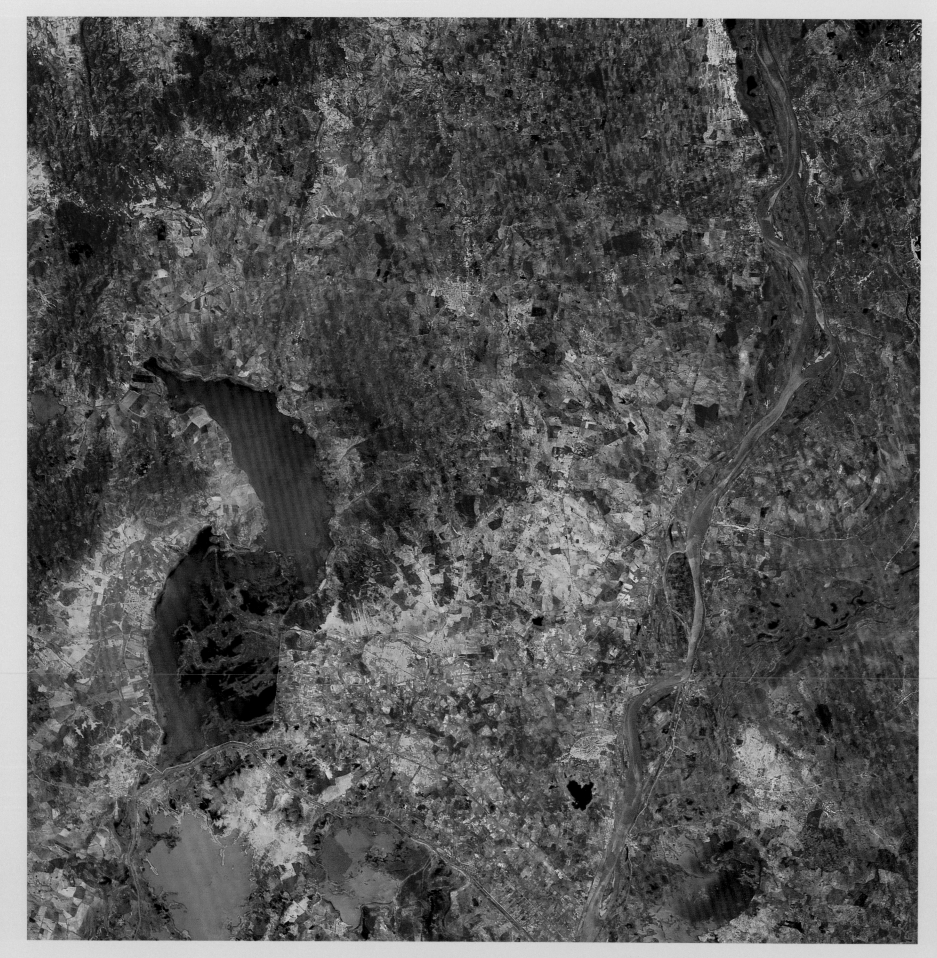

*Swamps bordering the Magdalena river between the provinces
of Bolívar and Magdalena, in Colombia.*

Col/41, page 71

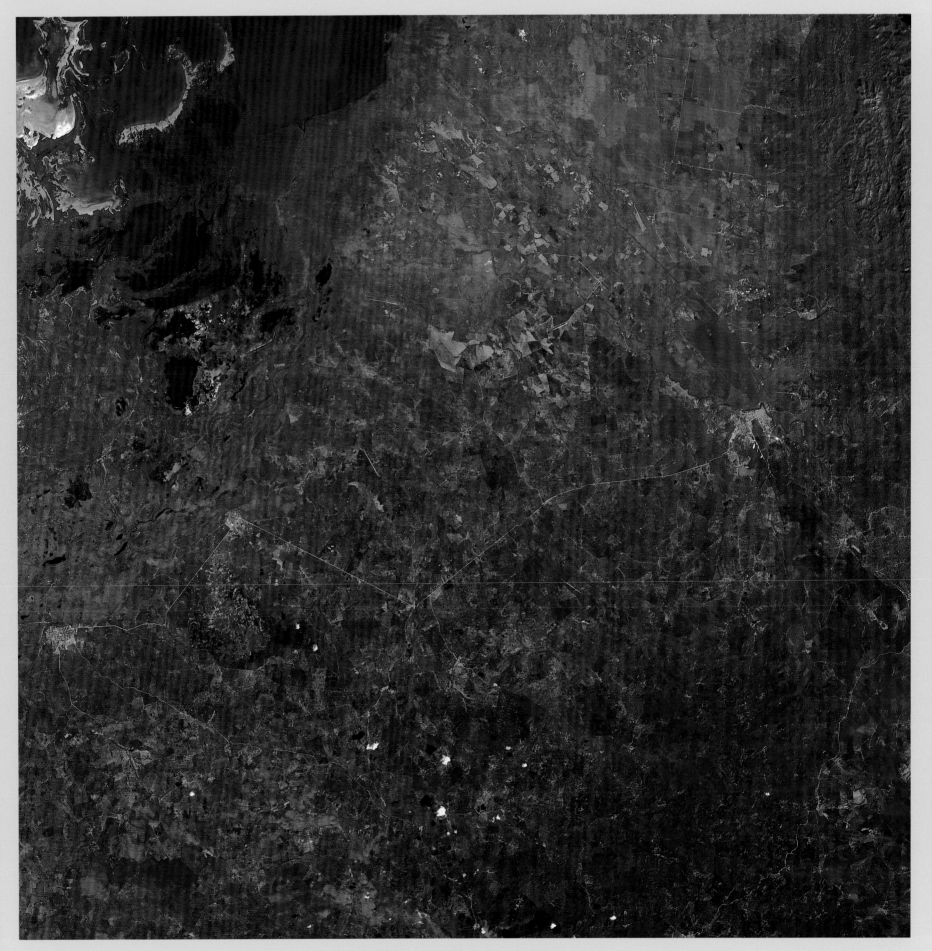

*Plains on the Colombian Caribbean
and Sierra Nevada de Santa Marta. Province of Magdalena.*

Col/42, page 71

*Golfo de Morrosquillo on Colombia's Caribbean coast between
the provinces of Sucre and Córdoba.*

Col/46, page 71

Bay of Cartagena, and the city of Cartagena de Indias.
Province of Bolívar.

Col/40, page 71

*Golfo de Morrosquillo on Colombia's Caribbean coast
between the provinces of Sucre and Córdoba.*

Col/45, page 71

*The Mompox depression between the provinces
of Bolívar and Magdalena, in Colombia.*

Col/44, page 71

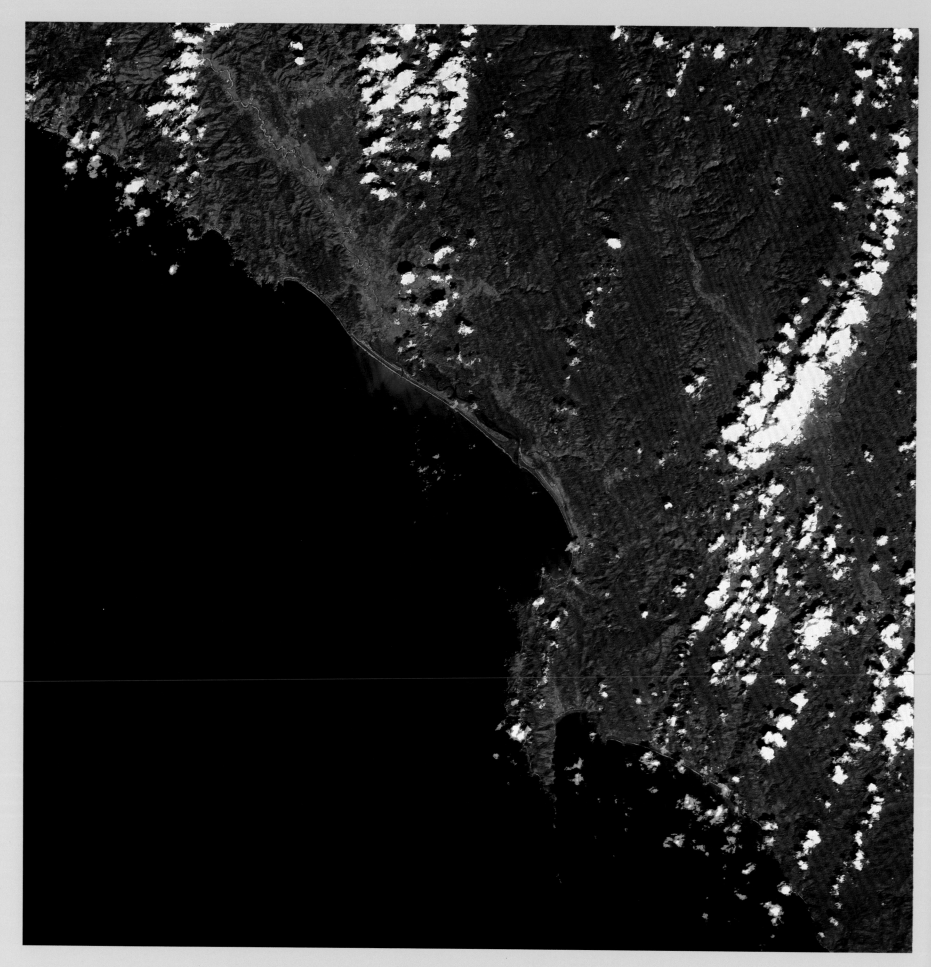

The Colombian Pacific coast
near the frontier with Panama. Province of Chocó.

Col/51, page 73

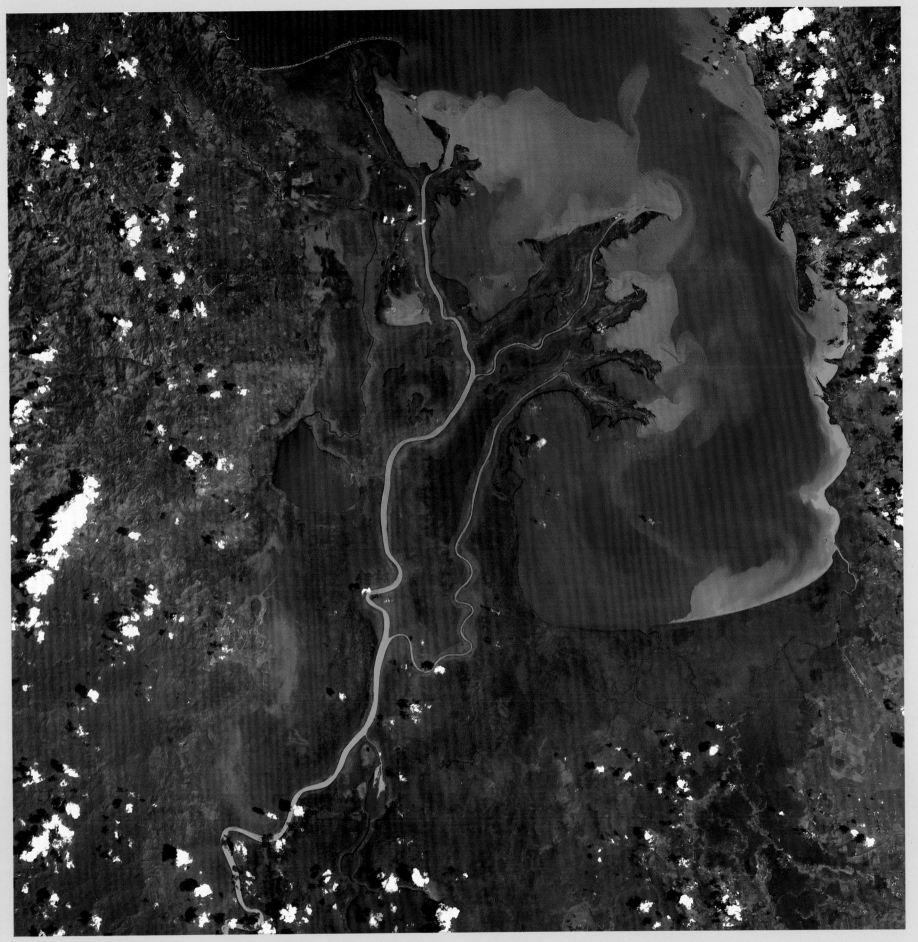

*Golfo de Urabá on Colombia's Caribbean coast,
in the provinces of Antioquia and Chocó.*

Col/50, page 73

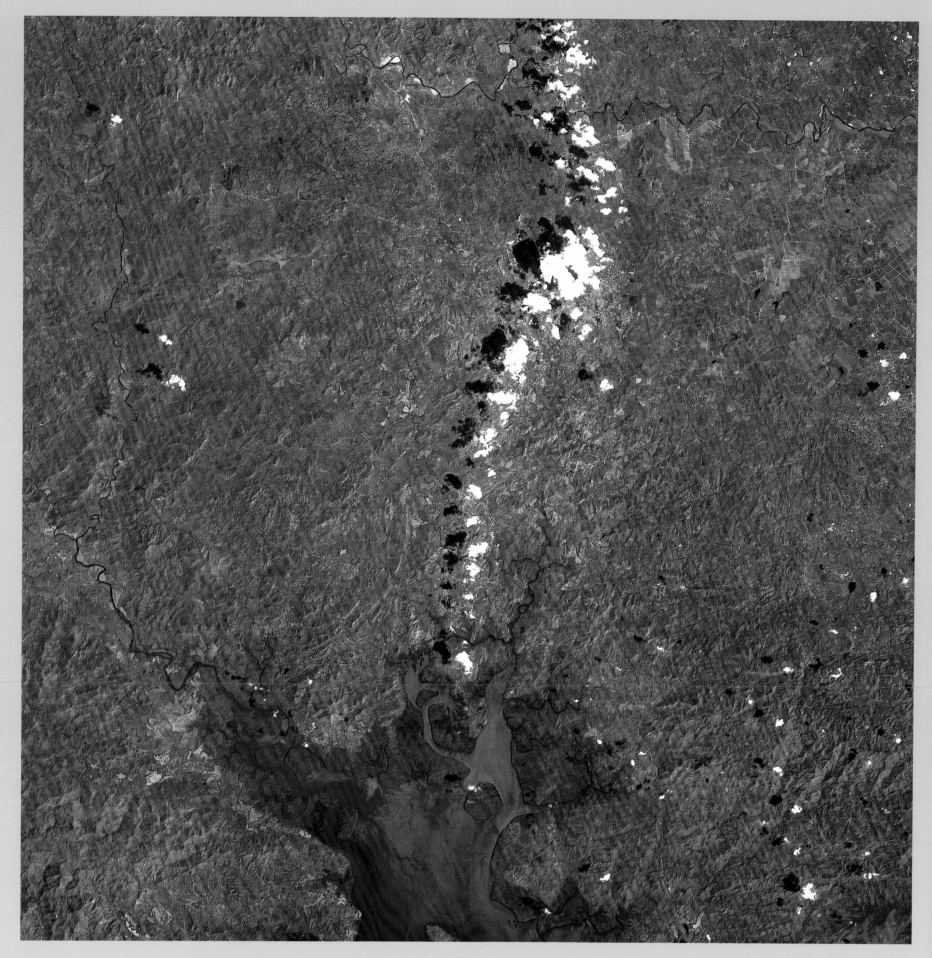

Peninsula of Azuero and Golfo de Montijo
in southern Panama.

Pan/49, page 72

*Gulf of Panama, Panama City
and Pacific entrance to the Canal.*

Pan/47, page 72

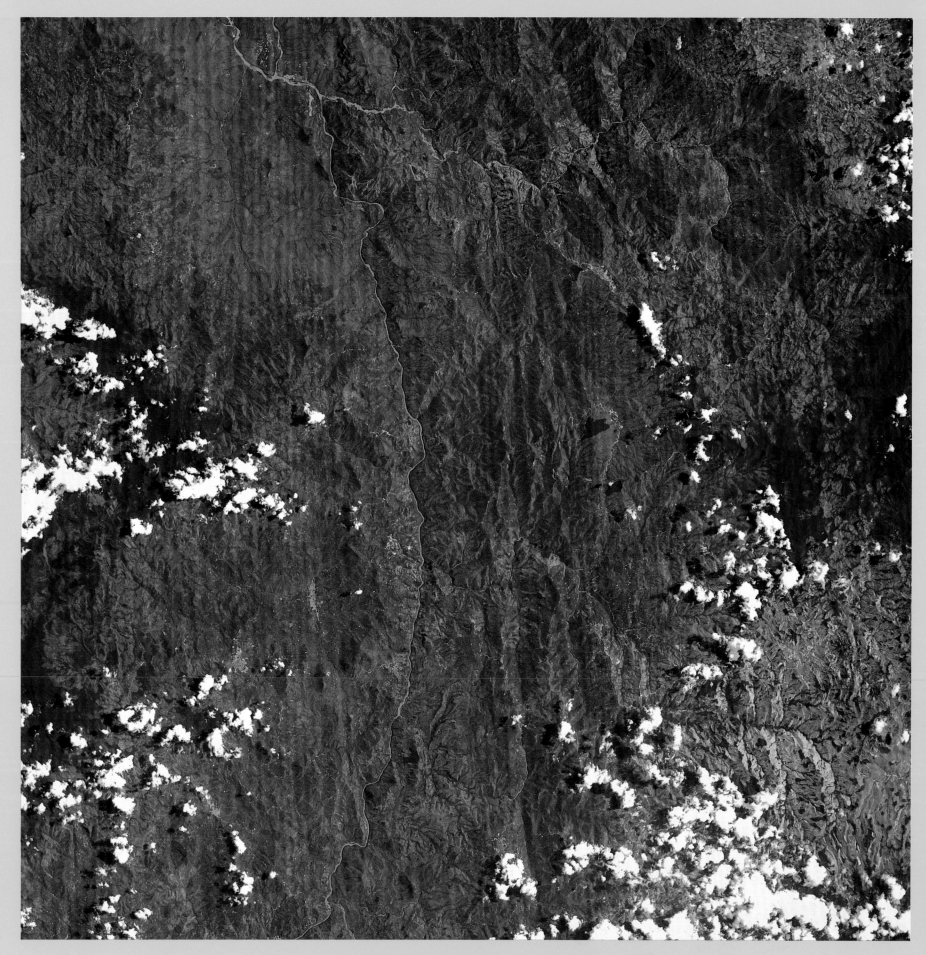

*Mountainous region of Colombia's Cordillera Central
in the provinces of Caldas and Antioquia.*

Col/52, page 74

*Cauca river between the Cordillera Central and Occidental in
the provinces of Caldas, Quindío, Risaralda and Valle.*

Col/53, page 74

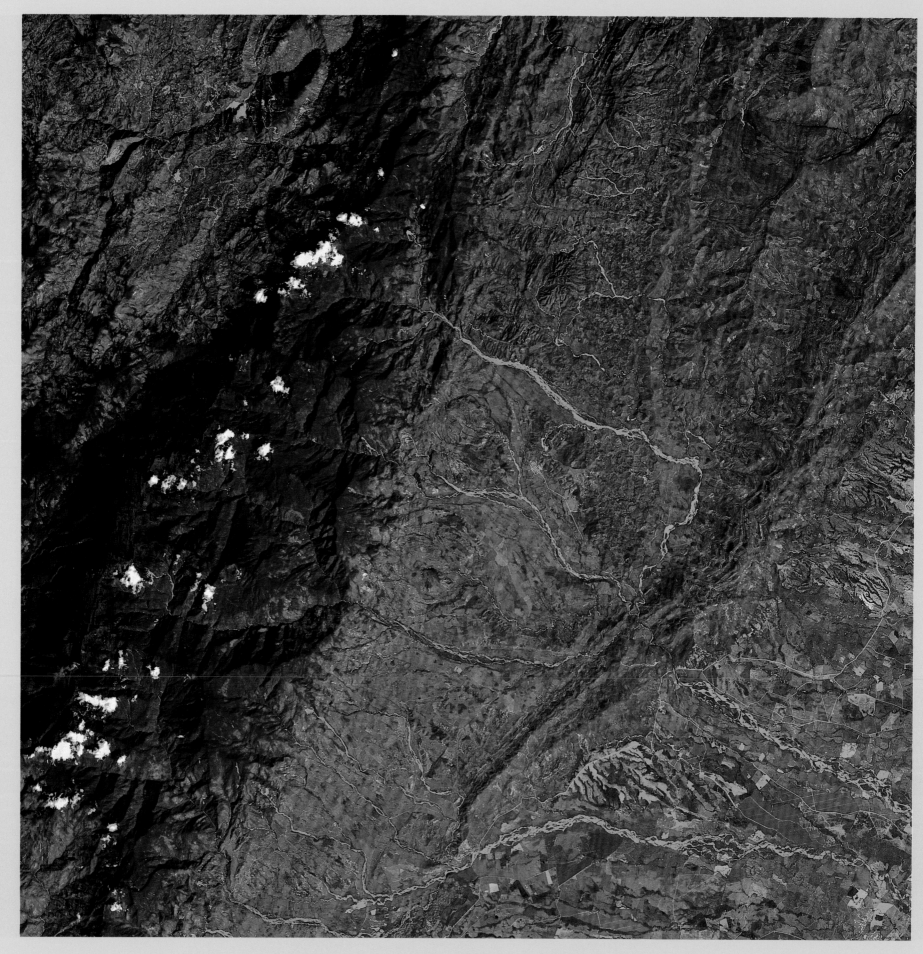

Foothills of the Colombian Cordillera Oriental overlooking the
Llanos in the provinces of Cundinamarca and Meta.

Col/56, page 75

*Region of the Colombian eastern Llanos
in the provinces of Meta and Casanare.*

Col/57, page 75

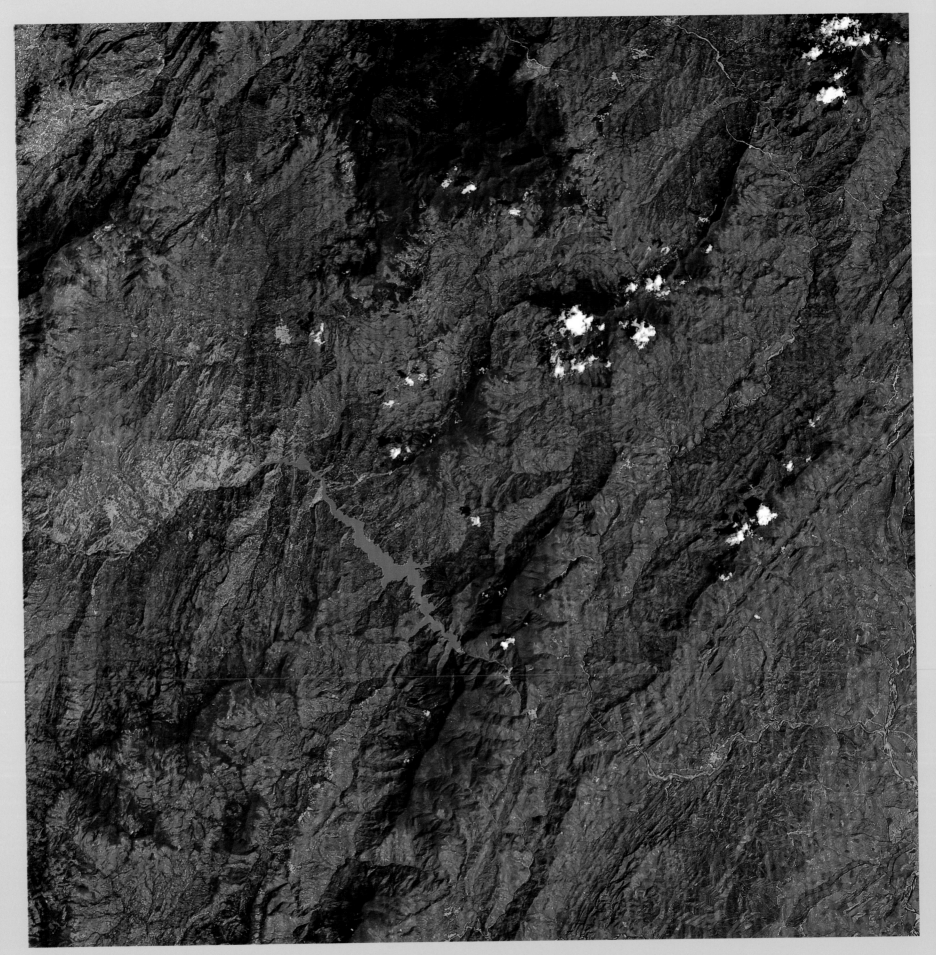

*The Colombian Cordillera Oriental
in the provinces of Boyacá and Cundinamarca.*

Col/54, page 75

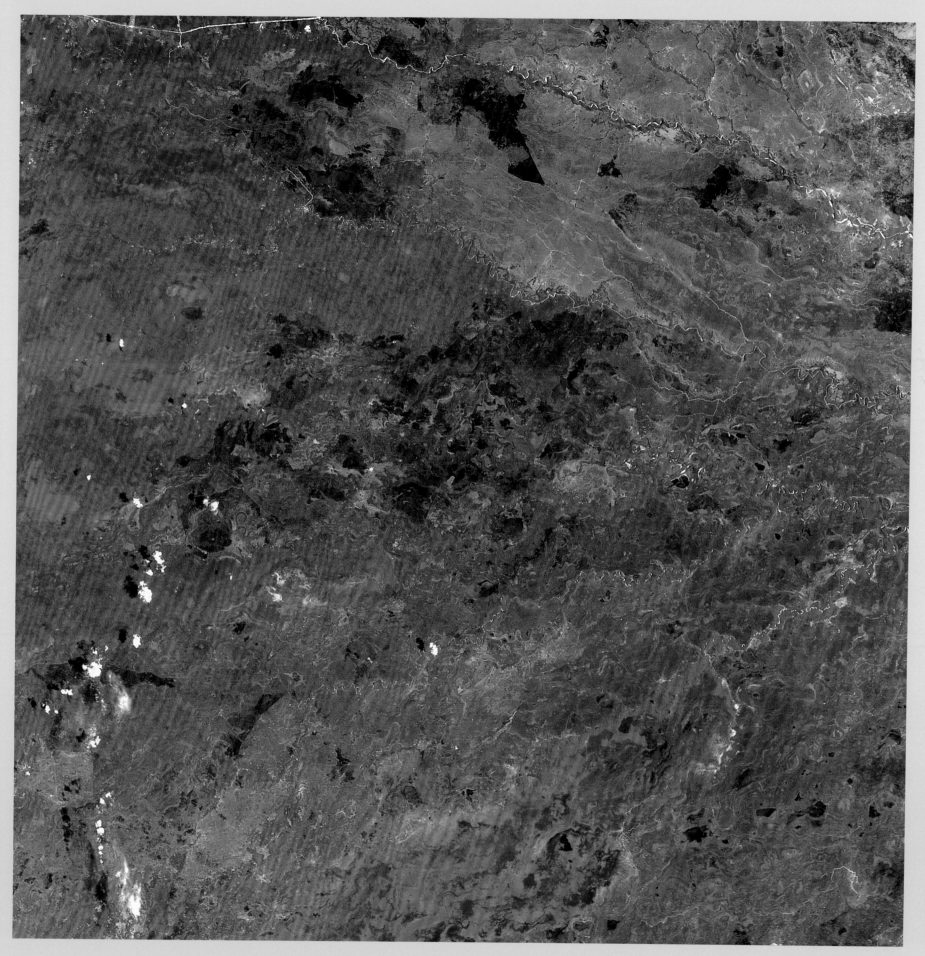

Region of Colombia's eastern Llanos.
Province of Arauca.

Col/58, page 76

Region of Colombia's eastern Llanos
in the provinces of Meta and Casanare.

Col/59, page 76

Llanos and jungle in eastern Colombia
near the border with Venezuela. Province of Vichada.

Col/61, page 77

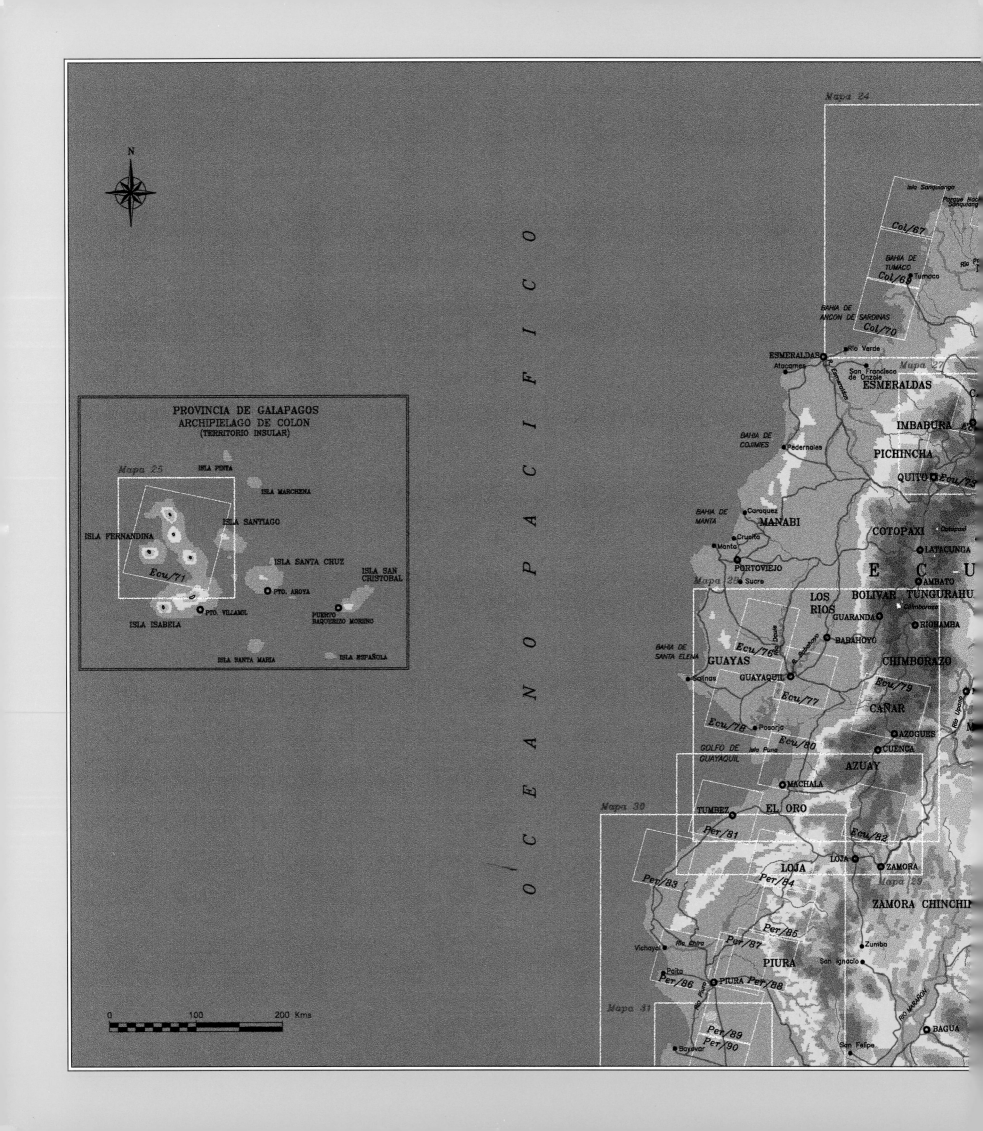

N

PROVINCIA DE GALAPAGOS
ARCHIPIELAGO DE COLON
(TERRITORIO INSULAR)

Mapa 25

ISLA PINTA

ISLA MARCHENA

ISLA SANTIAGO

ISLA FERNANDINA

Ecu/71

ISLA SANTA CRUZ

ISLA SAN
CRISTOBAL

PTO. AROYA

PTO. VILLAMIL

PUERTO
BAQUERIZO MORENO

ISLA ISABELA

ISLA SANTA MARIA

ISLA ESPAÑOLA

0   100   200 Kms

O C E A N O   P A C I F I C O

Mapa 24

Isla Sanguianga

*Parque Naci.
Sanguianga*

Col/67

*BAHIA DE
TUMACO*

Col/68

Tumaco

Rio Pa

*BAHIA DE
ANCON DE SARDINAS*

Col/70

ESMERALDAS

Rio Verde

Atacames

San Francisco
de Onzole

R. Esmeraldas

Mapa 27

ESMERALDAS

IMBABURA

*BAHIA DE
COJIMIES*

Pedernales

PICHINCHA

QUITO *Ecu/*

*BAHIA DE
MANTA*

Caraquez

MANABI

Crucita

Manta

COTOPAXI

Cotopaxi

LATACUNGA

PORTOVIEJO

E   C   U

Mapa 26 Sucre

AMBATO

LOS
RIOS

BOLIVAR TUNGURAHU.

GUARANDA

Chimborazo

*BAHIA DE
SANTA ELENA*

Ecu/76

R. Daule

BABAHOYO

RIOBAMBA

GUAYAS

R. Babahoyo

CHIMBORAZO

Salinas

GUAYAQUIL

Ecu/79

Rio Upano

Ecu/77

CAÑAR

Ecu/78

Posorja

Ecu/80

AZOGUES

CUENCA

*GOLFO DE
GUAYAQUIL*

Isla Puna

AZUAY

MACHALA

Mapa 30

TUMBEZ

EL ORO

Per/81

Ecu/82

LOJA

Per/83

LOJA

Per/84

ZAMORA

Mapa 29

ZAMORA CHINCHI

Per/85

Per/87

Zumba

Vichayal

Rio Chira

San Ignacio

Paita

PIURA

Per/86

PIURA *Per/88*

Rio Piura

Mapa 31

Per/89

Per/90

Bayovar

San Felipe

RIO MARAÑON

BAGUA

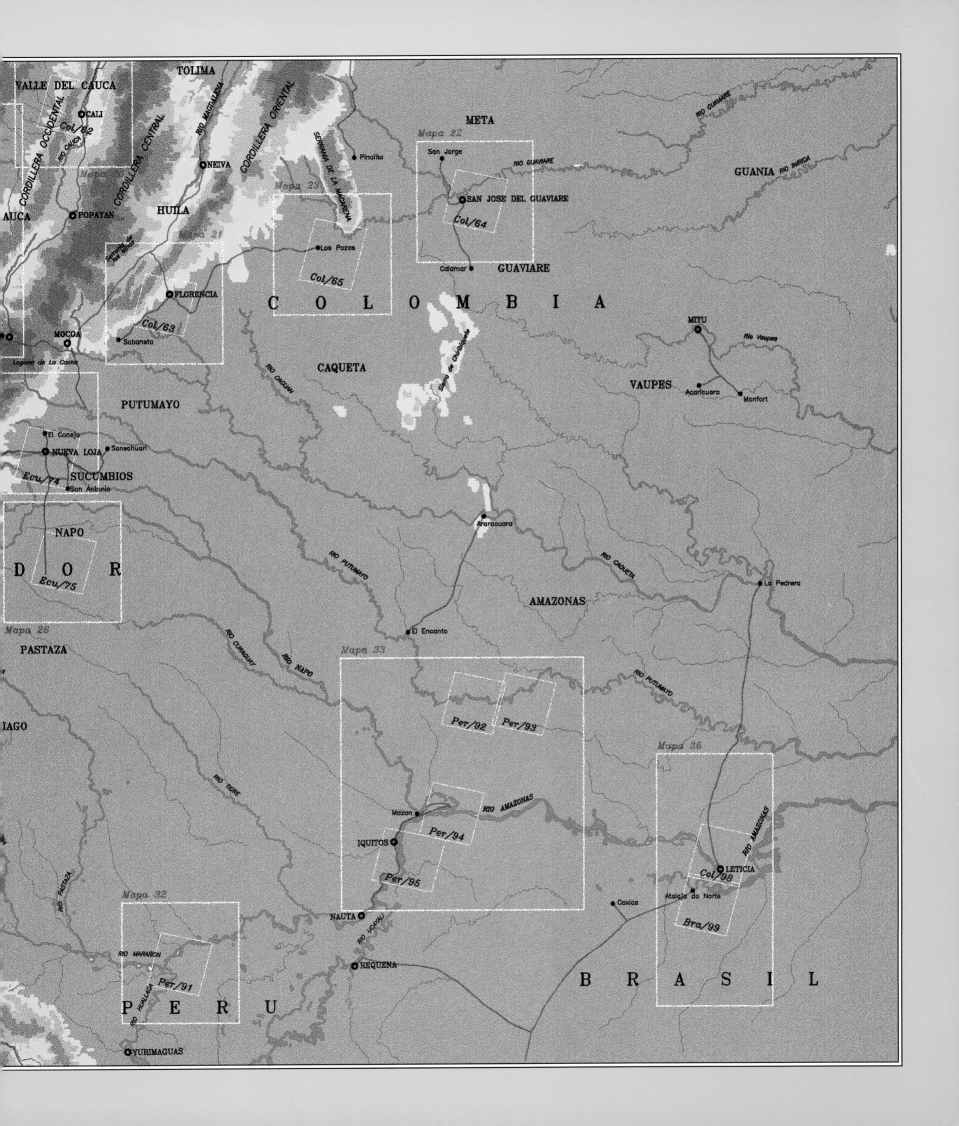

Col/62. Pg. 136.

Col/62. *City of Cali, in the Cauca river valley. Province of Valle del Cauca.* Page 136.

The city of Cali leans against the Cordillera Occidental and opens out to the east, south and north over the flat expanses of the Cauca river valley. The river, finding no obstacle on its path, is characterized by large meanders. The valley is widely populated. Besides Cali, with over 1.5 million people, there are the secondary towns of Yumbo, to the north, and Palmira, to the north-east. Agricultural activity is considerable, and revealed by the chequer pattern of fields, every inch of soil cultivated. Main crops are sugarcane, bananas, rice, cotton and corn. This intense production is reflected by the varied vegetal spectral signatures throughout the entire valley, which is explained by the different stage of growth and irrigation level of plantations. Depending on whether they're recently planted or ready to be harvested, crops present great variations of spectral signature.

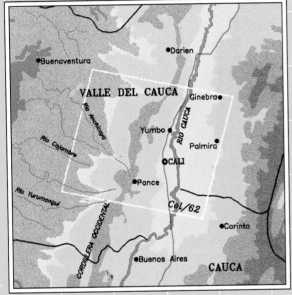

Map 20

Map 22

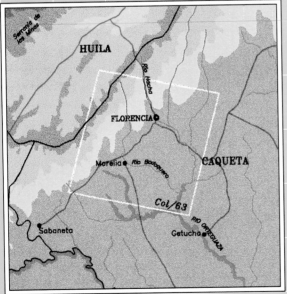

Map 21

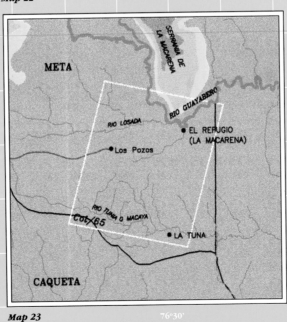

Map 23

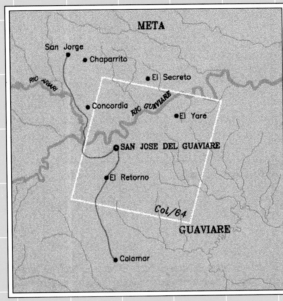

Col/63. Pg. 137.

Col/63. *Eastern foothills of Colombia's Cordillera Oriental in the province of Caquetá.* **Page 137.**

One clearly notes the transition between the mountain zone, in the northern part of the picture, and the jungle zone to the south, by the colours corresponding to different vegetations and by the creased and arid mountain configuration. Several rivers spring in the mountains, and rush down narrow valleys. The Hacha river flows through the city of Florencia, at the foot of the mountain. Further down its course, it is joined by a tributary, the Bodoquero, which springs in the Cordillera Oriental and passes through the small town of Morelia, at the foot of the mountain. The flat area has been systematically cleared, and the main activity is extensive cattle raising. Communication routes appear as straight lines on the plains.

Col/64. *Eastern Colombia's tropical rain forest. Province of Guaviare.* **Page 135.**

The Guaviare river, to the north-west of the picture, shows its lazy course, with its wide meanders, islands and sandbanks. The zone is covered with swamps formed by countless "dead" meanders. Most of the picture is occupied by tropical rain forest, with intense chlorophyllic activity reflected by a bright red spectral signature. Human presence is located in the small town of San José del Guaviare, with an airfield on the left bank of the Guaviare, on the outer curve of a meander. Colonization in the area spreads from the road inland, felling and burning trees to open up clearings and fields. The irregular shape of these open spaces reveal uncontrolled and almost indiscriminate colonization. There are no organized groups of settlers exploiting the woodlands in rational fashion. Deforestation is perpetrated according to the needs of the last-arrived settlers and the market price of wood, or other products extracted from the forest. The green squares of cattle fields are surrounded by black squares, possibly burnt clearings. Roads serve as bridgeheads to exploit and tear down the forest. The technical originality of this picture lies in the tiny colour streaks sliced between normal spectral signatures. These "parasites", typical of the South American and Pacific sector, are electrons and protons shooting down from Van Allen's Belt.

Col/64. Pg. 135.

Col/65. Pg. 134.

Col/65. *Eastern Colombia's tropical rain forest in the province of Meta.* **Page 134.**

The curve of the Guayabero river is caused by the southern tip of the Serranía de La Macarena, which stretches a little further north of the picture. The Guayabero is joined by a tributary, the Losada, which springs in the eastern foothills of the Cordillera Oriental. The zone shows evidence of non-organized human settlements, by the large burnt patches in black. One observes several fires, with billows of white smoke blown by the north-south wind. The village visible further south of the Guayabero is La Macarena, which has an airstrip, like most settlements in this zone with no land access. To the south of the picture, man-perpetrated deforestation creates a vegetation transitional between pasture and woodland, composed of grass and shrubs, appearing in green and grey.

Col/66. *River deltas of the Colombian Pacific coast in the provinces of Cauca and Nariño. Page 139.*

One observes the estuaries and deltas of rivers with variable courses which flow into the Pacific. The northern delta is fed by the Naya, to the north, and San Juan de Micay, to the south. The central delta receives the southern branch of the San Juan de Micay, and, in the southern delta, several minor rivers form immense branches with relatively small courses. All these deltas have given birth to particularly luxuriant zones of mangrove swamps and coastal aquatic jungle. One can observe that these mangrove swamps show a different spectral signature than the tropical rain forest further inland. The former are bright red due to intense chlorophyllic activity generated by the permanent presence of water, whereas the latter is dark red, owing to a slower vegetal rhythm. Because of the heavy rains, the alluvial cones of the rivers carry immense amounts of vegetal matter and produce extensive corollas in the sea. The zone is practically uninhabited, due to its situation between jungle and ocean in an area of exceptionally heavy rainfall.

Col/67. *Colombian Pacific coast near the frontier with Ecuador.*

The coast shows a very spread-out aspect, with the deltas and estuaries of several rivers, which have created islands by cutting off fragments of the shore. The largest river is the Patía, to the south of the picture, which forms a northward bend before flowing into the ocean. The vegetation, composed of mangrove swamps and tropical rain forest, shows in a shade of red characteristic of intense chlorophyllic activity directly related to the region's heavy rains. One detects the presence of keys and small islands along the coastline, by the white barrier at sea on the mouth of the deltas. Surf is also noticeable by furrowed parallel lines on the ocean close to the shore. Human settlements in the zone are too tiny to be visible.

Col/68. *Mangrove swamps on the Colombian Pacific coast, in the province of Nariño.* **Page 138.**

The estuaries belong to the Guapi and, further west, Iscuandé rivers. Besides revealing a sluggish current due to the absence of relief, the meanders add an artistic touch to the picture: indeed they look like snakes writhing on a red carpet of tropical trees. The rainy season is denoted by the wide alluvial cones of the rivers, the estuaries of which are very sandy, showing in white. Next to the coastal mangrove swamp strip, the forest has an extremely dense, impenetrable aspect, until it reaches the eastern foothills of the Cordillera Occidental. The only human presence is the small town of Guapí, on the left bank of the river of the same name, after the curve of the delta. There are very few open spaces indicating cultivated fields, as the main human activity is fishing.

Map 24

Col/69. *Bahía de Tumaco on Colombia's Pacific coast, in the province of Nariño, near the frontier with Ecuador.* **Page 30.**

The wide Bahía de Tumaco is surrounded by mangrove swamps, amidst branches of the Mira river delta, to the south. The bay receives the course of other rivers, through natural canals, the formation of which was facilitated by the coast's marshy environment. The town of Tumaco lies to the south side of the bay, on the islands at the outlet, the southernmost inhabited zone on Colombia's Pacific coast. The old airstrip is built on the furthest island, communicating with the town by a bridge. Another airstrip is located further to the east, on the continent, by the shore of the bay. The town was established on the islands: their exposure to ocean winds confer them a climate healthier to human settlement. One also observes the road and pipeline coming from the country's interior.

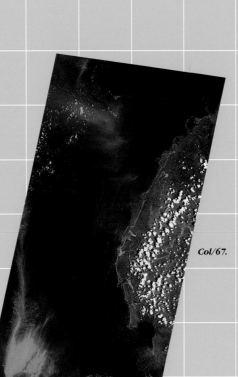

Col/66. Pg. 139.

Col/68. Pg. 138.

Col/67.

Col/69. Pg. 30.

Col/70. Pg. 11.

Col/70. *Cabo Manglares and estuary of a branch of the Mira river on the Colombian Pacific coast, near the border with Ecuador.* **Page 11.**

One observes Cabo Manglares, well-defined by the estuary of a branch of the Mira river. The wide course of the river, which springs in the Ecuadorian Andes, carries large amounts of organic and vegetal matter, noticeable in its final corolla. The coastal vegetation is usually composed of mangrove swamps, which explains the scarce human presence. The only visible town, behind Tola island and within the delta, is San Lorenzo, the first settlement on Ecuador's northern Pacific coast. A road leading to the south-east links it to the continent. The shallowness of the canal waters can be discerned by the paler colour of the bottom, and by the sand and mudbanks formed by the gradual sedimentation of the estuaries. Finally, one notes the differences in cloud formations: compact and globular over the land, and stringy over the sea. This depends on the volume of water evaporation, and the temperature of the surface under the clouds.

Ecu/71. Pg. 17.

Ecu/72. *City of Ibarra in the Ecuadorian Andes, near the border with Colombia. Province of Imbabura.* Page 140.

This region of the Andes stretches north of Quito, at 3,000 m. above sea level. Here lies the city of Ibarra, on the road leading to Tulcán and the Colombian border. Local agriculture is overwhelmingly characterized by a system of small farmlands, dating back to the Incas, growing corn, potatoes and vegetables. One observes Ibarra to the south of the picture, and the mountain relief totally formed of volcanic ash and clay.

Ecu/71. *Galapagos islands in the Colón archipelago, which belongs to Ecuador, over a thousand kilometres away.* Page 17.

The Galapagos islands, situated at a distance of more than a thousand kilometres from the Ecuadorian coast, are bathed by the cold Humboldt Current, which gives birth to a wildlife of eminent importance. This haven of rare species of turtles, seals, dolphins and birds is protected by UNESCO. In the picture, one observes Fernandina island to the west, the big Isabela island in the centre and Santiago island to the right. The picture enables to clearly distiguish the formation of the islands, shaped by the agglomeration of lava flows from successive eruptions. Isabela island is a good example. Composed exclusively of volcanic rock and ash, the islands have vegetation on the side receiving the most rain. On those appearing in the picture, one notes the vegetation growth on the south-eastern side: which means that rains tend to fall along the same axis. The islands are uninhabited, due to conditions hostile to humans: water is non-existent, and vegetation scarce. Moreover, flora and fauna are under official safeguard. One distinguishes streaks of obnoxious "free" electrons from Van Allen's Belt, responsible for erasing radiometric recordings.

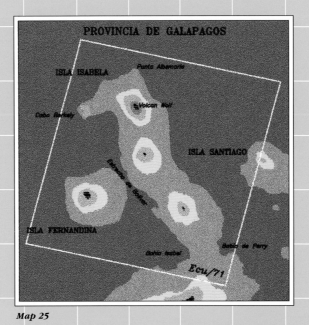

Map 25

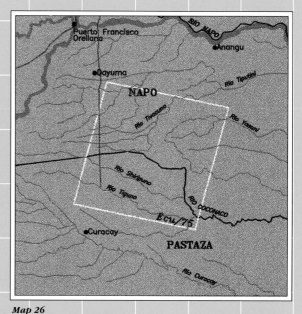

Map 26

Map 27

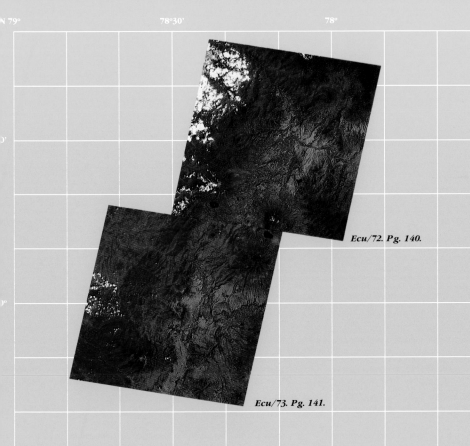

Ecu/72. Pg. 140.

Ecu/73. Pg. 141.

Ecu/74. Pg. 142.

Ecu/75. Pg. 143.

Ecu/73. *Quito, the Ecuadorian capital, in the*
Andean Cordillera. Province of Pichincha.
Page 141.

Quito, founded in 1534, lies at the foot of the
Pichincha volcano, to the west, on uneven terrain
overlooking the valley of the Machangara river. The
Cayambe volcano looms to the north-east. With a
population of 1.2 million, the Ecuadorian capital is the
country's second largest city after Guayaquil. Its
extension north-south is more than 25 km., but east-
west only three or four km. The city grew around the
historical centre and railway station for Guayaquil, and
along the Pan-American highway. More recently,
urban development has spread to the Iñaquito valley
and environs of the airport, which is now well within
the city's perimeter.

Ecu/74. *Recent settlement in Ecuador's tropical*
rain forest. Province of Napo. **Page 142.**

One observes the town of Nueva Loja in the proximity
of the Aguarico river. Since the early seventies, the
zone is Ecuador's major source of oil, and the town
and its refinery sprang up at the time of the boom.
One can distinguish six oil-storage tanks. A
government colonization policy followed in the wake
of the bonanza, and many impoverished inhabitants of
the Andes were sent to stake their claim in this
territory, of strategic value for its resources and
proximity to the Colombian border. One clearly notes
the methodical pattern of settlement, with individual
plots. The jungle is being gradually burnt down, and
allotted to immigrants by the Ecuadorian government.
Colonization systematically proceeds to the east and
south, on the bend of the Coca river.

Ecu/75. *Jungle and meandering rivers in eastern*
Ecuador, near the frontier with Peru. **Page 143.**

The frontier was defined in 1942 by the *Protocolo de*
Rio de Janeiro. One observes the meanders of the
Coconaco river, a southern tributary of the Napo.
Radiometers register high chlorophyllic activity and
the total lack of human presence, except for the
rectilinear route of a road to the south-west, the first
symptom of the arrival of civilization.

Ecu/76. *Outskirts of Guayaquil and Guayas valley in Ecuador's coastal region.* Page 149.
Peripheral zone north of Guayaquil in the Guayas valley, through which the Daule flows before emptying into the Guayas delta, further west. The region is savannah, irrigated and devoted to the oilseed and rice industry. All the produce goes to Guayaquil, for export. In the middle of the fields, one observes the village of Pedro Carbo, on a curve of the Daule.

Ecu/77. *Guayas delta and Guayaquil, on the Ecuadorian Pacific.* Page 148.
Here, urban development has to deal with an amphibian environment, where coastal mangrove swamps give way to humid savannah crossed by a saltwater canal system, flooded by tides. Guayaquil, with almost two million people, owes its wealth to the export of locally-grown rice and oilseeds, and extensive shrimp-farming, one of the country's main sources of revenue. Shrimp farms, spread along the Guayas canals, appear in the picture as black rectilinear fields.

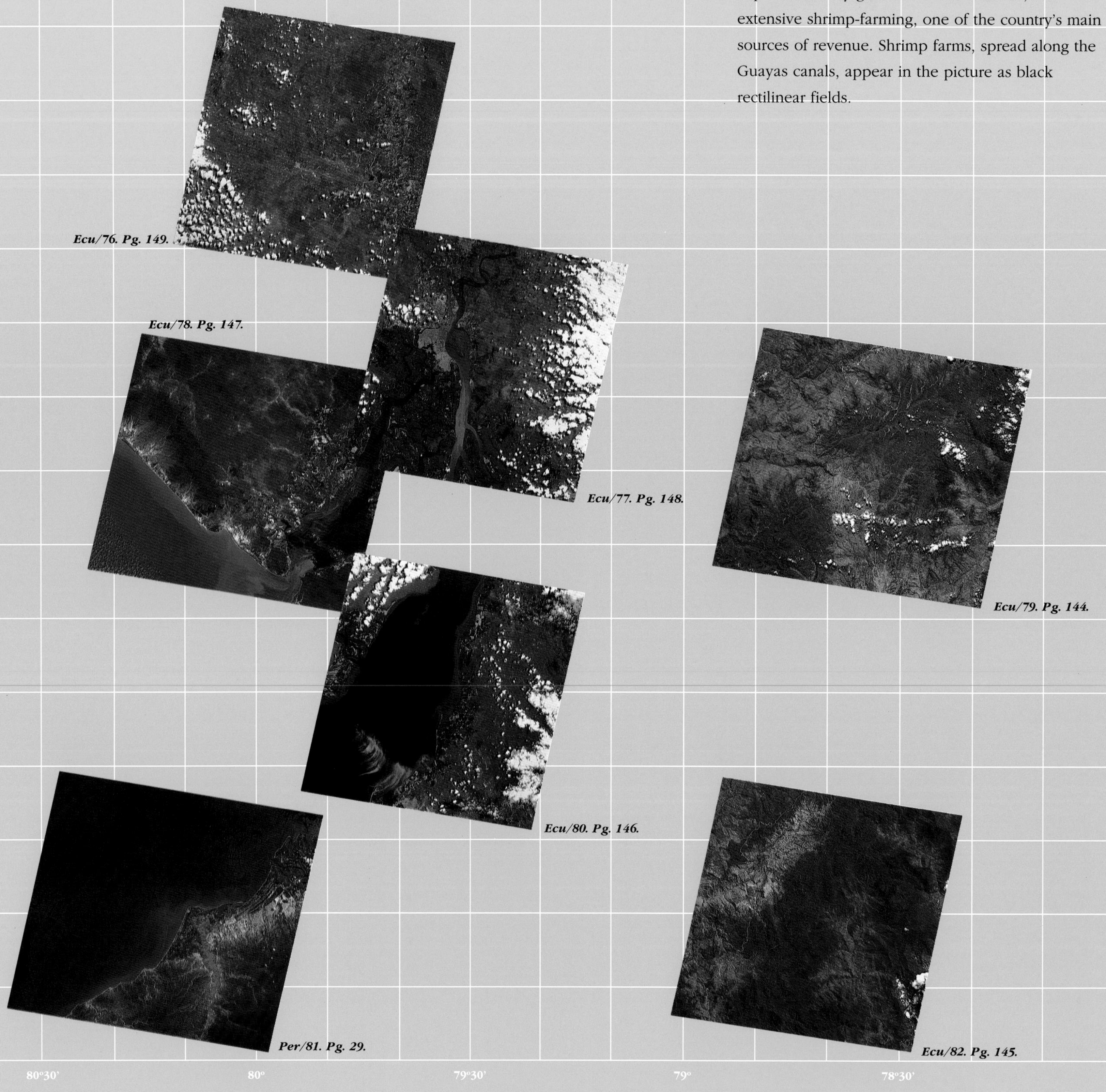

Ecu/76. Pg. 149.
Ecu/78. Pg. 147.
Ecu/77. Pg. 148.
Ecu/79. Pg. 144.
Ecu/80. Pg. 146.
Per/81. Pg. 29.
Ecu/82. Pg. 145.
80°30'
80°
79°30'
79°
78°30'
78°
1°30'
2°
2°30'
3°
3°30'
4°

Ecu/78. *Outskirts of the city of Guayaquil, Puná island and estuary of the Guayas river.* Page 147.

Puná island, to the southeast of Guayaquil, and estuary of the Guayas river with its muddy, shallow waters and mangrove swamps, which are being slowly destroyed and replaced by shrimp farms.

Ecu/79. *Arid stretches of Ecuador's southern Andes. Province of Azuay.* Page 144.

This zone of deep inner valleys and outer slopes spread around the city of Cuenca, to the south of the country, which acts as a regional centre of agricultural development. It's a transition zone between the "avenue of volcanoes" and the lake district in southern Ecuador.

Ecu/80. *Pacific coast and estuary of the Guayas river in southern Ecuador, near the border with Peru.* Page 146.

This mangrove swamp region of Ecuador's Pacific coast, near the frontier with Peru, in the latitudes of the Guayas river estuary and the Jambelí canal, in the Gulf of Guayaquil, is the world's greatest shrimp producer, with over 100,000 tons a year, three quarters of which harvested in the the Machala city canal, in the southern part of the picture.

Per/81. *Coastal desert and town of Tumbes in northern Peru, near the frontier with Ecuador.* Page 29.

In an almost totally desert zone, the town of Tumbes, a citrus fruit and vegetable producer, appears in the picture next to the red river course. Further north, the small border town of Zarumilla, surrounded by mangrove swamps, is mainly devoted to shrimp farming, which can be discerned by the black lines on the sea slowly invading the coast.

Ecu/82. *Páramo de Matanga in Ecuador's southern Andes, near the Peruvian town of Tumbes.* Page 145.

This region, close to the border with Peru, is formed by deep inner valleys and outer slopes. An arid landscape is noted on the bare slopes of the mountains where the road passes through.

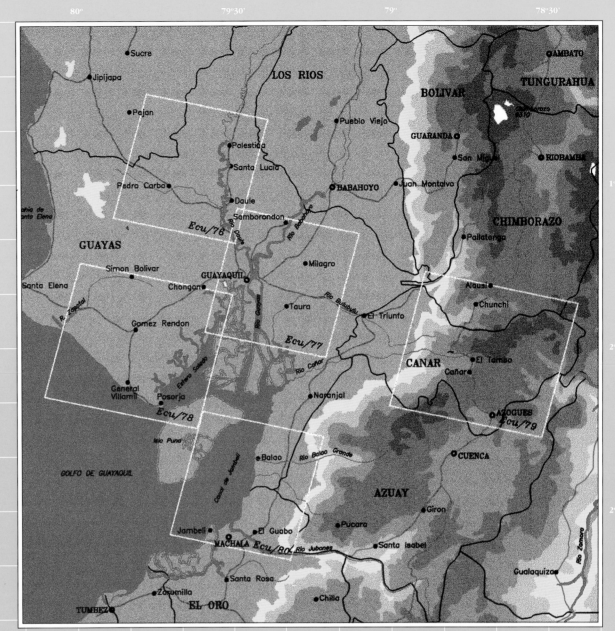

Map 28

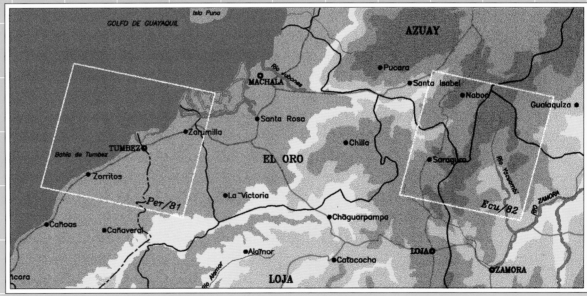

Map 29

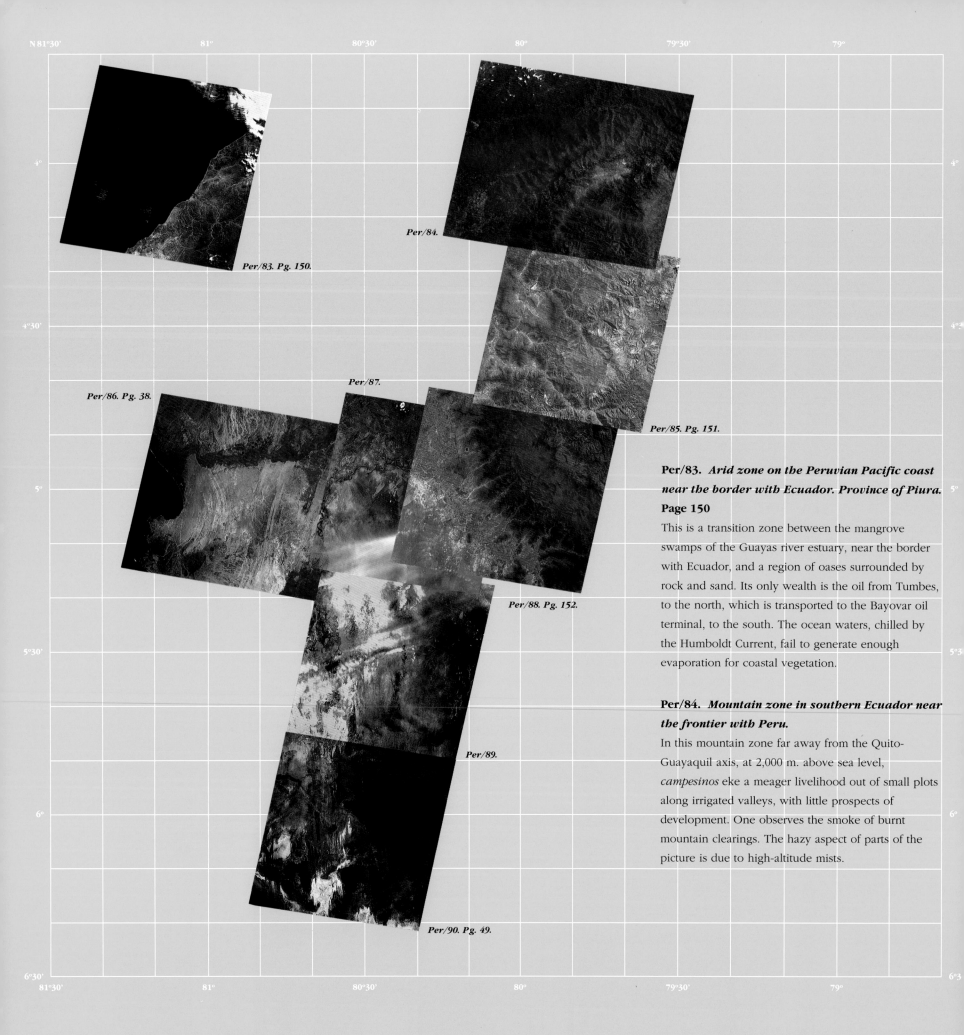

Per/83. Pg. 150.

Per/84.

Per/86. Pg. 38.

Per/87.

Per/85. Pg. 151.

Per/88. Pg. 152.

Per/89.

Per/90. Pg. 49.

Per/83. *Arid zone on the Peruvian Pacific coast near the border with Ecuador. Province of Piura.* **Page 150**

This is a transition zone between the mangrove swamps of the Guayas river estuary, near the border with Ecuador, and a region of oases surrounded by rock and sand. Its only wealth is the oil from Tumbes, to the north, which is transported to the Bayovar oil terminal, to the south. The ocean waters, chilled by the Humboldt Current, fail to generate enough evaporation for coastal vegetation.

Per/84. *Mountain zone in southern Ecuador near the frontier with Peru.*

In this mountain zone far away from the Quito-Guayaquil axis, at 2,000 m. above sea level, *campesinos* eke a meager livelihood out of small plots along irrigated valleys, with little prospects of development. One observes the smoke of burnt mountain clearings. The hazy aspect of parts of the picture is due to high-altitude mists.

Per/85. *Vast mountain slopes on the border between Peru and Ecuador. Province of Piura.* Page 151.

This zone sees the continuation of the Andes from Ecuador into Peru. The Ecuadorian town of Macará, located on the river of the same name, lies on the border. The Macará river, in a west-east direction, marks the border between the two countries; further down, its name changes to Río Blanco. The zone, of strategic significance, is traditionally settled by Indians from the Andean Cordillera.

Per/86. *Bahía de Paita and estuary of the Chira river in northern Peru's coastal desert.* Page 38.

In a totally arid environment, the harbour of Paita, visible at the bottom of the bay, exports the local phosphates. To the east, a road links it to the city of Piura. Further north, the town of Sullana, on the Chira river, is connected to Piura by a desert road. One distinguishes agricultural activity by the red rectangles.

Per/87. *Aspect of "La Chala", Peru's Pacific coastline desert, in the province of Piura.*

The only water supply in this barren region is the Piura river, which crosses the picture after flowing down from the cordillera to irrigate fields on its path. Further south lies the city of Piura, with 300,000 people, the resources of which are phosphates from the south and oil from the north. The presence of a high-altitude cloud veils the south-eastern part of the picture.

Per/88. *Transition zone between Peru's Pacific coast desert and the foothills of the Cordillera.* Page 152.

In the south-western part of the picture, in the environs of Piura, one sees the desert; further east, farmlands in valleys at the foot of mountain stream gorges; and finally, to the north-east, the first slopes of the cordillera. The small town of Chulucanas lies in the agriculturally-developed area.

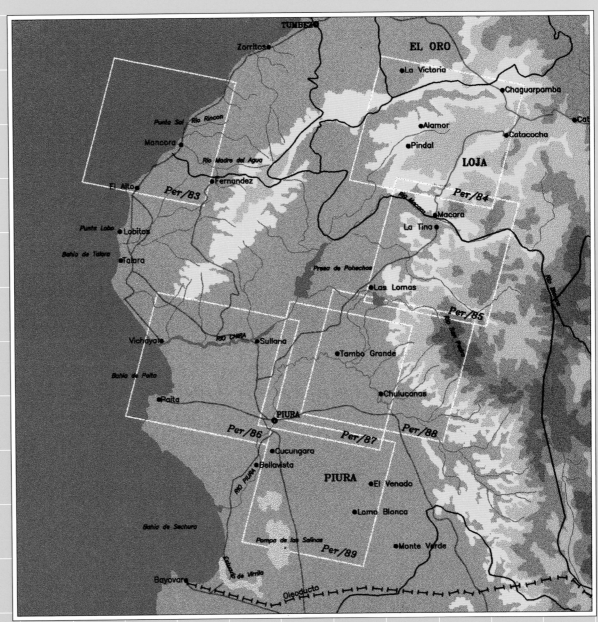

Map 30

Per/89. *Desert region on northern Peru's Pacific coast in the province of Piura.*

On the coastal desert of "La Chala", one notes the presence of oases which supply a variety of agricultural produce to the entire region. High nebulousness unables us to define exactly the nature of relief and human activities.

Per/90. *Bahía de Sechura on Peru's coastal desert, south of the town of Piura.* Page 49.

One observes the rectilinear paths of the roads and pipelines which link the south of the country to the coast. The white spots indicate "dead" lakes of sand and salt.

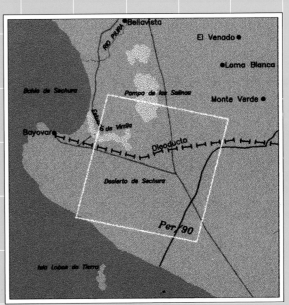

Map 31

Per/91. *Confluence of the Huallaga and Marañón rivers in the Peruvian Amazon jungle.* Page 42.

One notes the lazy, muddy and meandering course of the rivers, and, in the southern part of the picture, the small town of Lagunas, on the right bank of the Huallaga river, with burnt clearing settlements. Following the left bank of the Marañón river towards Iquitos, to the north-east, one observes the rectilinear path of the pipeline funnelling oil to refineries in the Andes. In the eastern part of the picture, a high-altitude lenticular cloud formation reflects the sun and conceals the land below.

Per/92. *Border area between Peru and Colombia, on the Putumayo river.*

This picture corresponds to the zone west of picture Per/91. On Peruvian territory, one observes the course of the Algodón river before flowing into the Putumayo to the east.

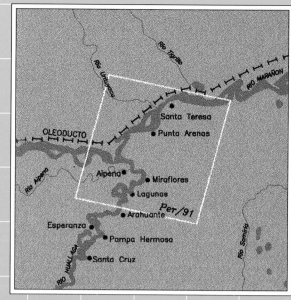

Mapa 32

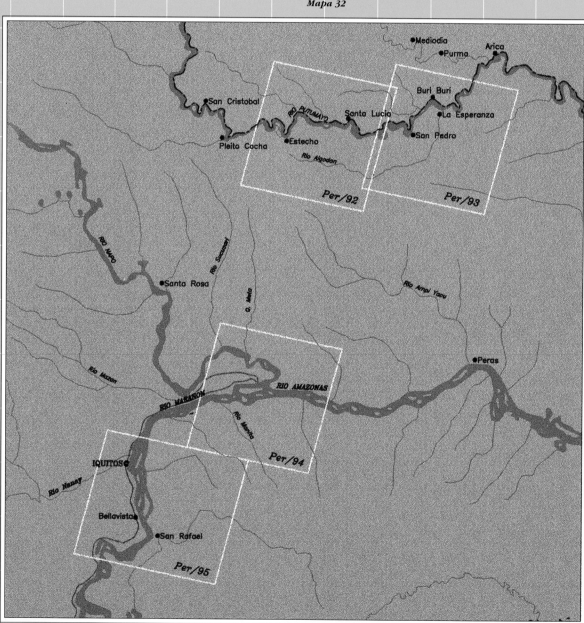

Per/91. Pg. 42

Map 33

Per/93. *Putumayo river on the border between Peru and Colombia.* **Page 153.**

One observes the confluence between the Algodón river, a small grey-blue snake climbing up from the south, and the pale green Putumayo. On the Colombian side of the Putumayo, i.e. on its left bank, one notes a human settlement, the village of Buri-Buri, only accessible by the river as there's no airstrip. The clouds gathering in the south-western part of the picture form a uniform shroud, which covers the entire zone almost permanently.

Per/94. *Confluence of the Marañón and Amazon rivers, north-east of Iquitos.* **Page 155.**

Two giant rivers of the Amazon jungle unite to form the Amazon, which flows into the Atlantic far to the east. One notes a cultivated stretch and, further along, a few burnt patches ready to be farmed. Next to these fields is an airstrip.

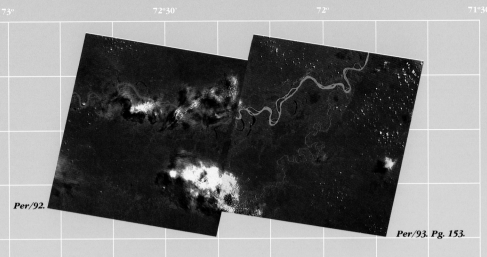

Per/92.

Per/93. Pg. 153.

Per/94. Pg. 155.

Per/95. Pg. 154.

Per/95. *City of Iquitos on the Marañon river in north-eastern Peru's Amazon jungle.* **Page 154.**

This city of 200,000 people is the most important in Peru's Amazon *Oriente*. It owes its development and growth to oilfields spread over the entire region; the production is refined up in the Andes. A strong wave of colonization, stretching along roads close to the city, followed the discovery of oil.

Per/96. *Course of a minor tributary of the Ucayali river in the Peruvian Amazon jungle.*

In the immensity of the jungle, one observes small deforested patches on the riverbank, which are only accessible by boat.

Per/97. *City of Pucallpa on the Ucayali river, a tributary of the Marañon, in the Peruvian Amazon jungle.*

On the muddy, sluggish and meandering course of the Ucayali, which is born of the confluence of the Urubamba and Tambo rivers, the city of Pucallpa was founded, the first zone of settlement downstream from the cordillera from the Andean "gateway" of Huánuco. Its agricultural produce is mainly cassava, rice and fruit. One can see the road leading from Pucallpa to the cordillera. Plains stretch along this vital artery, but never very deep. A branch of this road follows the course of the Aguaytia, a tributary of the Ucayali, to the north-west.

Per/96.

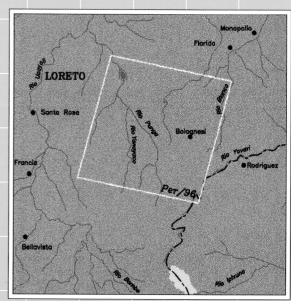

Map 34

Per/97.

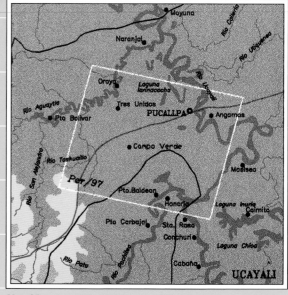

Map 35

Col/98. *City of Leticia on the border between Colombia, Peru and Brazil, in the Amazon jungle.* Page 156.

The dense jungle appears like a sea of vegetation, of an unmarred purple. On this stretch, the Amazon river is two kilometres wide, with the presence of islands and meanders indicating a sluggish flow over soft terrain. On the right bank, one notes traces of ancient beds of the Amazon, with "dead meanders". One observes greater soil resistance on the north bank, which fails to show traces of former courses. Human presence is practically limited to the city of Leticia, on Colombian territory, with its chequer pattern and two airfields. The zone's relative colonization occurs along the road and river. In general fashion, human settlements are fragile and disorganized. Several airstrips, unidentified on maps, can be seen in the middle of the jungle, as little white streaks.

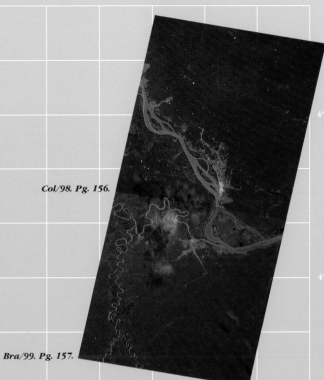

Col/98. Pg. 156.

Bra/99. Pg. 157.

Bra/99. *The Brazilian Amazon jungle, south of the Amazon river and its tributary Yavarí.* Page 157.

The countless "dead meanders" of the Yavarí river form, near the confluence, transient lakes in the form of closed curves. The smallest river, which flows up from the south, is the Itacuaí, the course of which lies entirely within Brazilian territory. On its confluence with the Yavarí, one notes the village of Atalaia do Norte, linked by a road to the locality on the confluence of the Yavarí and Amazon. These settlements resort to fluvial transport for survival and trade with other centres downstream, until Leticia in Colombia and Tabatinga in Brazil.

Map 36

*Eastern Colombia's tropical rain forest
in the province of Meta.*

Col/65, page 121

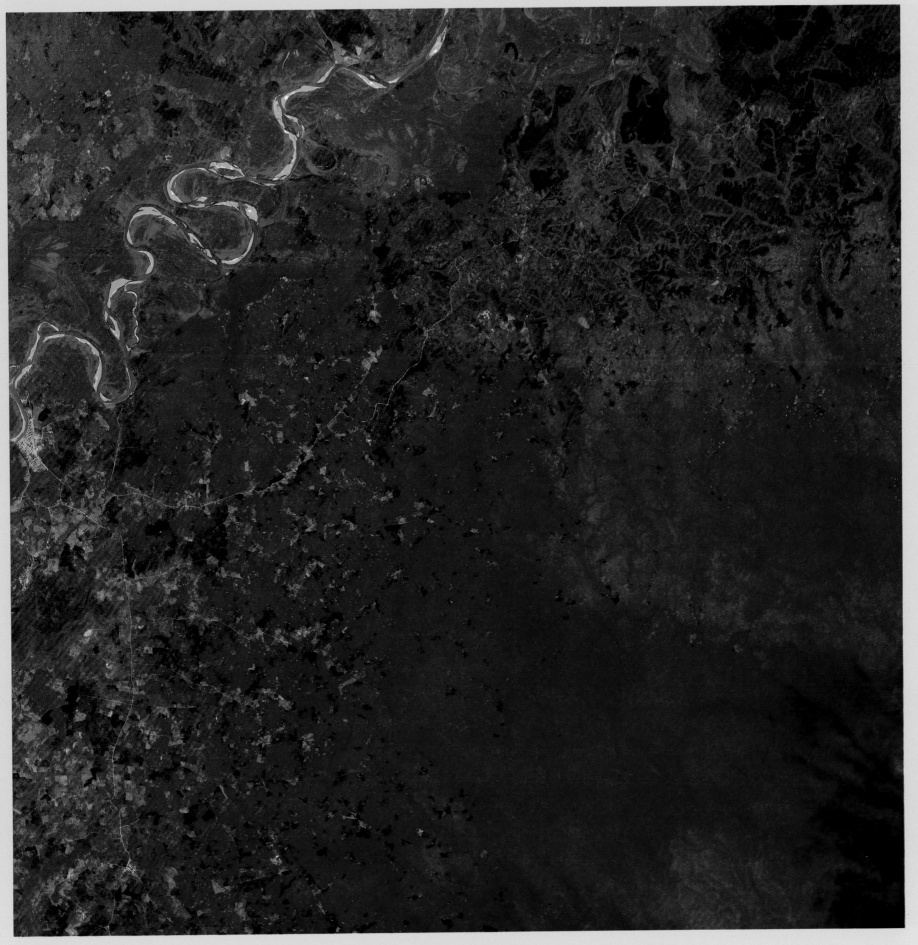

Eastern Colombia's tropical rain forest.
Province of Guaviare.

Col/64, page 121

City of Cali, in the Cauca river valley.
Province of Valle del Cauca.

Col/62, page 120

Eastern foothilis of Colombia's Cordillera Oriental
in the province of Caquetá.

Col/63, page 120

*Mangrove swamps on the Colombian Pacific coast,
in the province of Nariño.*

Col/68, page 123

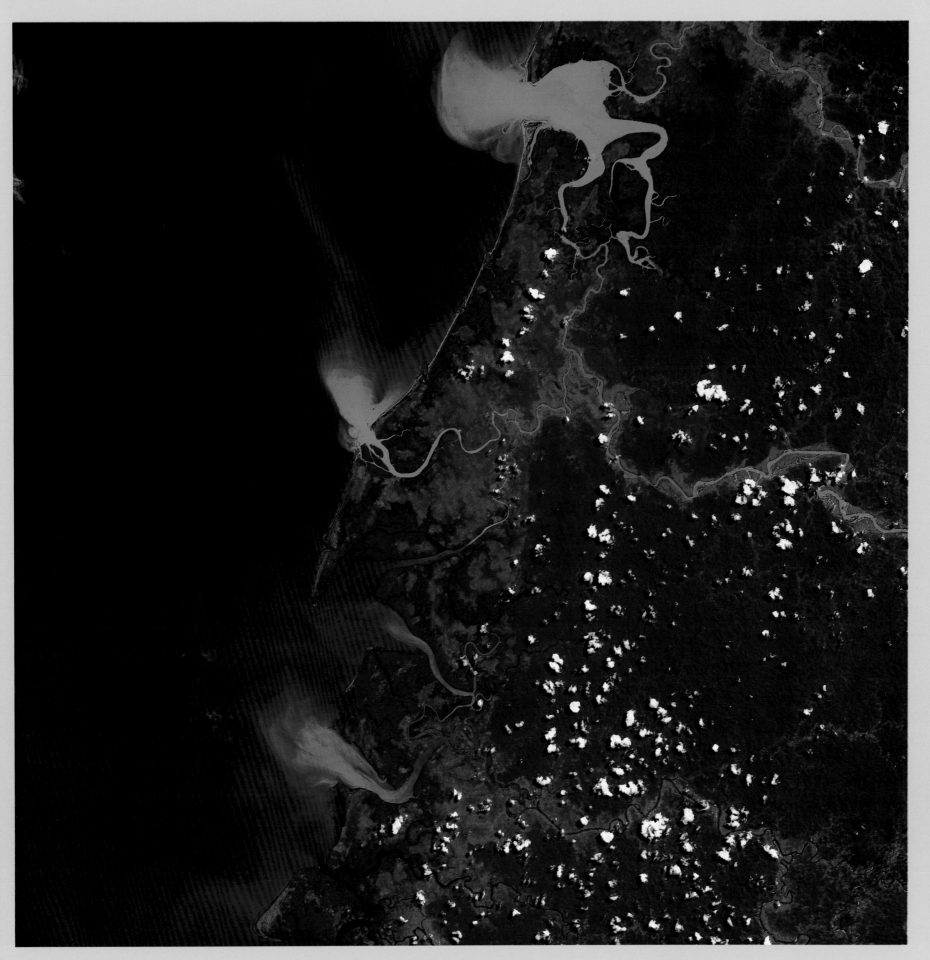

*River deltas of the Colombian Pacific coast
in the provinces of Cauca and Nariño.*

Col/66, page 123

City of Ibarra in the Ecuadorian Andes,
near the border with Colombia. Province of Imbabura.

Ecu/72, page 125

*Quito, the Ecuadorian capital,
in the Andean Cordillera. Province of Pichincha.*

Ecu/73, page 125

Recent settlement in Ecuador's tropical rain forest.
Province of Napo.

Ecu/74, page 125

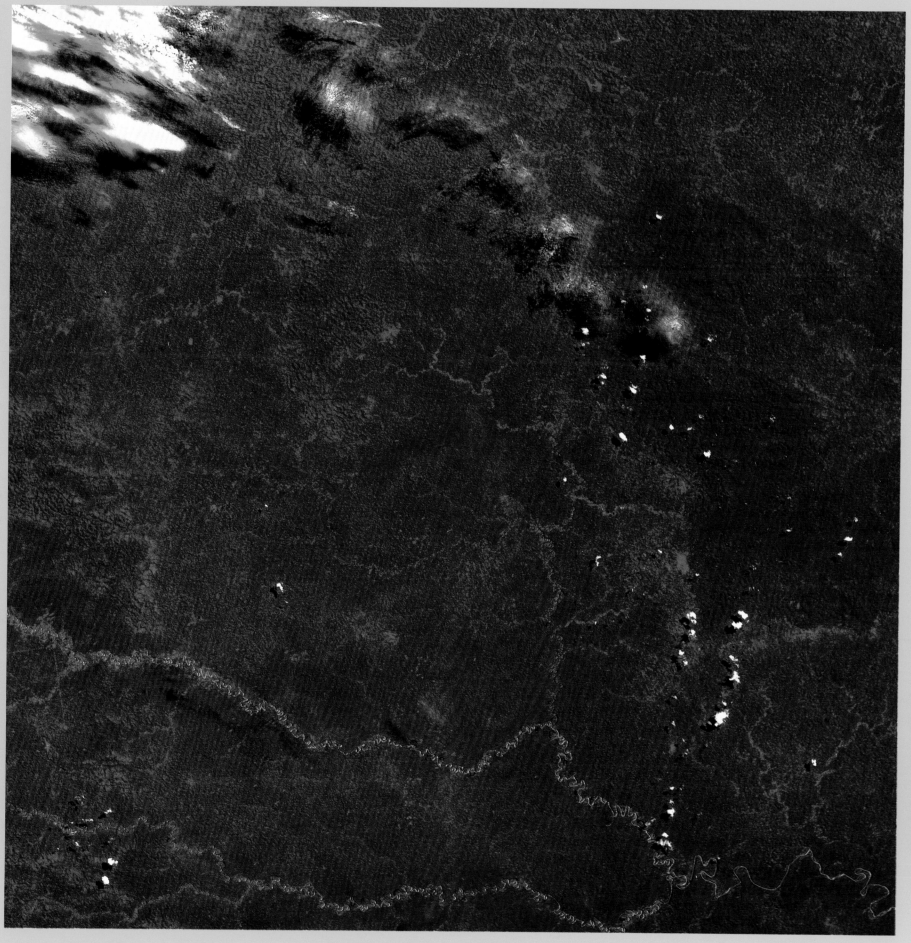

Jungle and meandering rivers in eastern Ecuador,
near the frontier with Peru.

Ecu/75, page 125

Arid stretches of Ecuador's southern Andes.
Province of Azuay.

Ecu/79, page 126

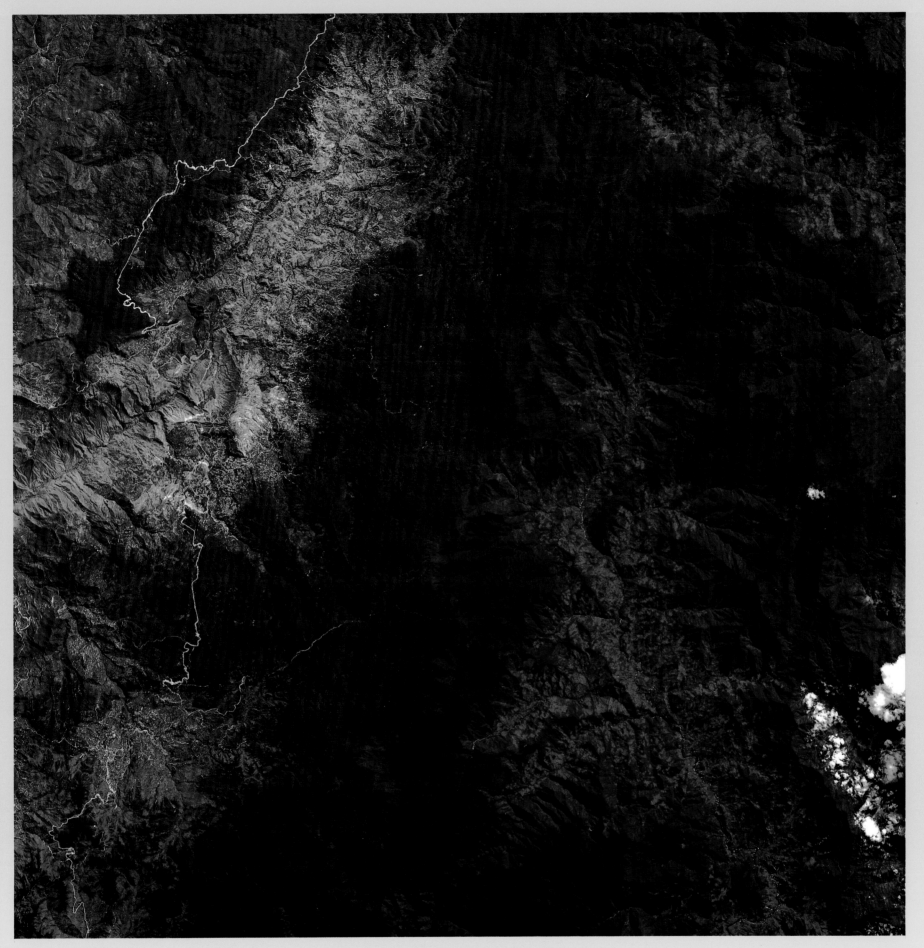

Páramo de Matanga in Ecuador's southern Andes,
near the Peruvian town of Tumbes.

Ecu/82, page 126

*Pacific coast and estuary of the Guayas river
in southern Ecuador, near the border with Peru.*

Ecu/80, page 126

146

*Outskirts of the city of Guayaquil, Puná Island
and estuary of the Guayas river.*

Ecu/78, page 126

Guayas delta and Guayaquil,
on the Ecuadorian Pacific.

Ecu/77, page 126

*Outskirts of Guayaquil and Guayas valley
in Ecuador's coastal region.*

Ecu/76, page 126

Arid zone on the Peruvian Pacific coast
near the border with Ecuador. Province of Piura.

Per/83, page 128

Vast mountain slopes on the border
between Peru and Ecuador. Province of Piura.

Per/85, page 128

*Transition zone between Peru's Pacific coast desert
and the foothills of the Cordillera.*

Per/88, page 128

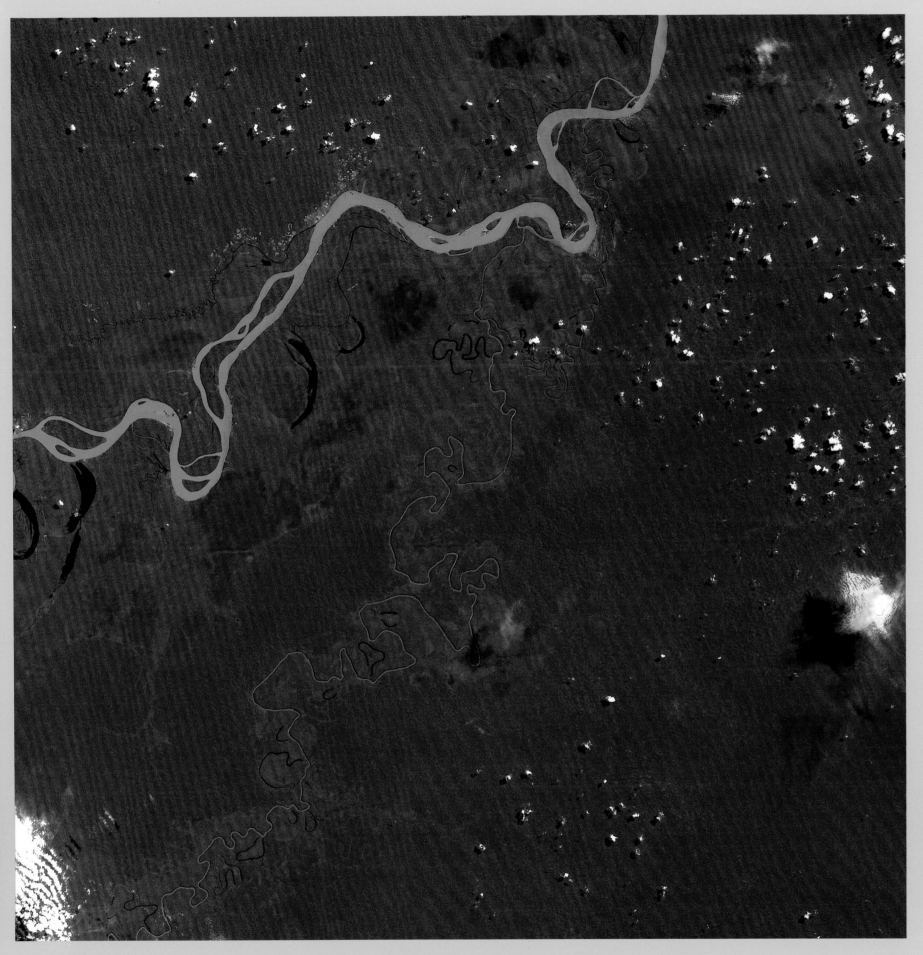

Putumayo river on the border
between Peru and Colombia.

Per/93, page 131

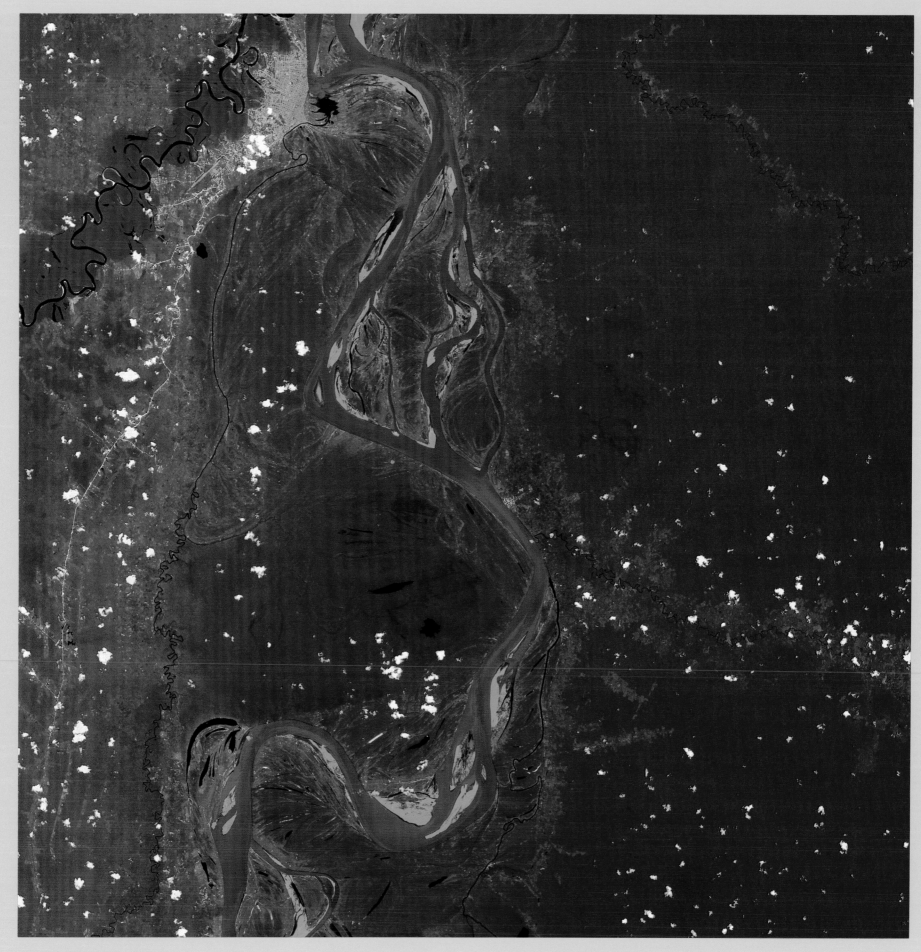

City of Iquitos on the Marañón river
in north-eastern Peru's Amazon jungle.

Per/95, page 131

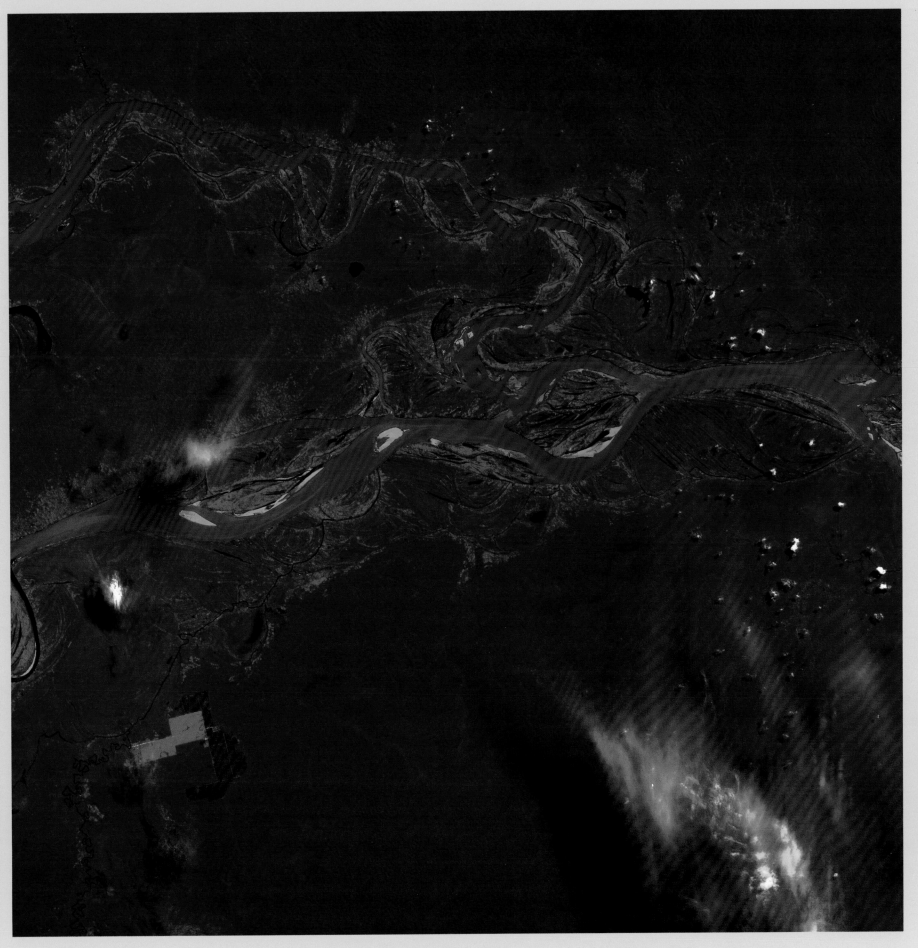

Confluence of the Marañón and Amazon rivers,
north-east of Iquitos.

Per/94, page 131

City of Leticia on the border between Colombia,
Peru and Brazil, in the Amazon jungle.

Col/98, page 133

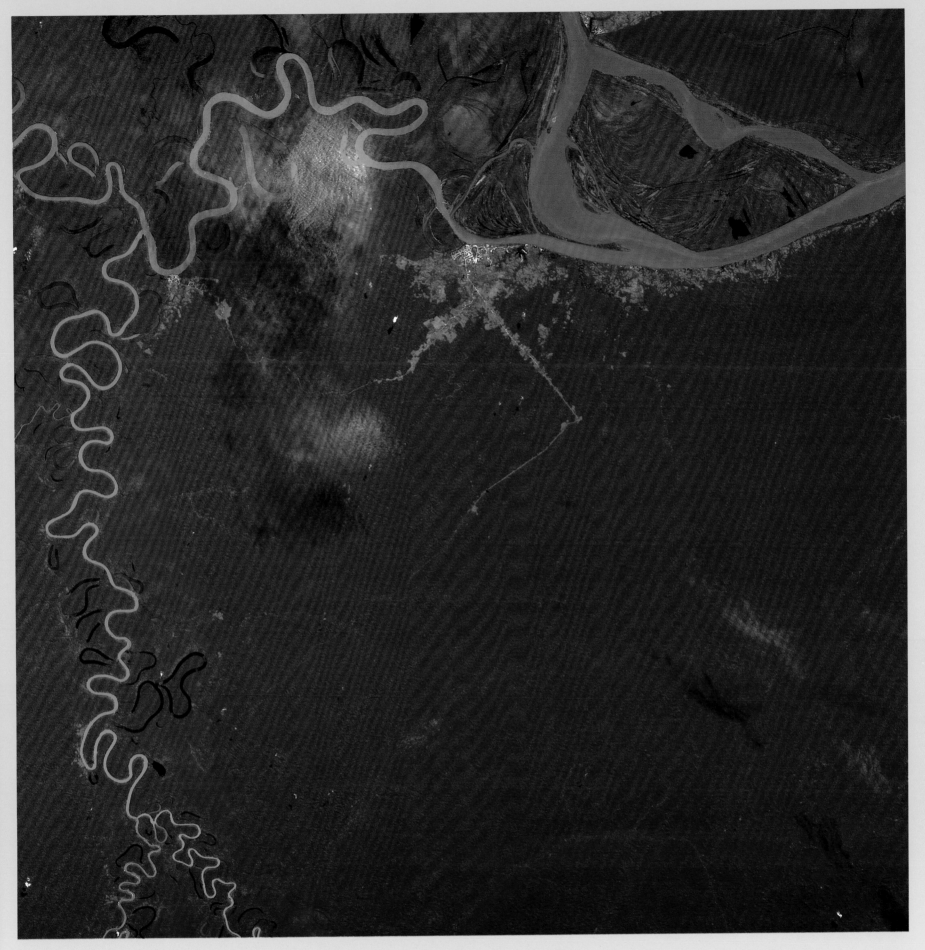

*The Brazilian Amazon jungle, south of the Amazon river
and its tributary Yavarí.*

Bra/99, page 133

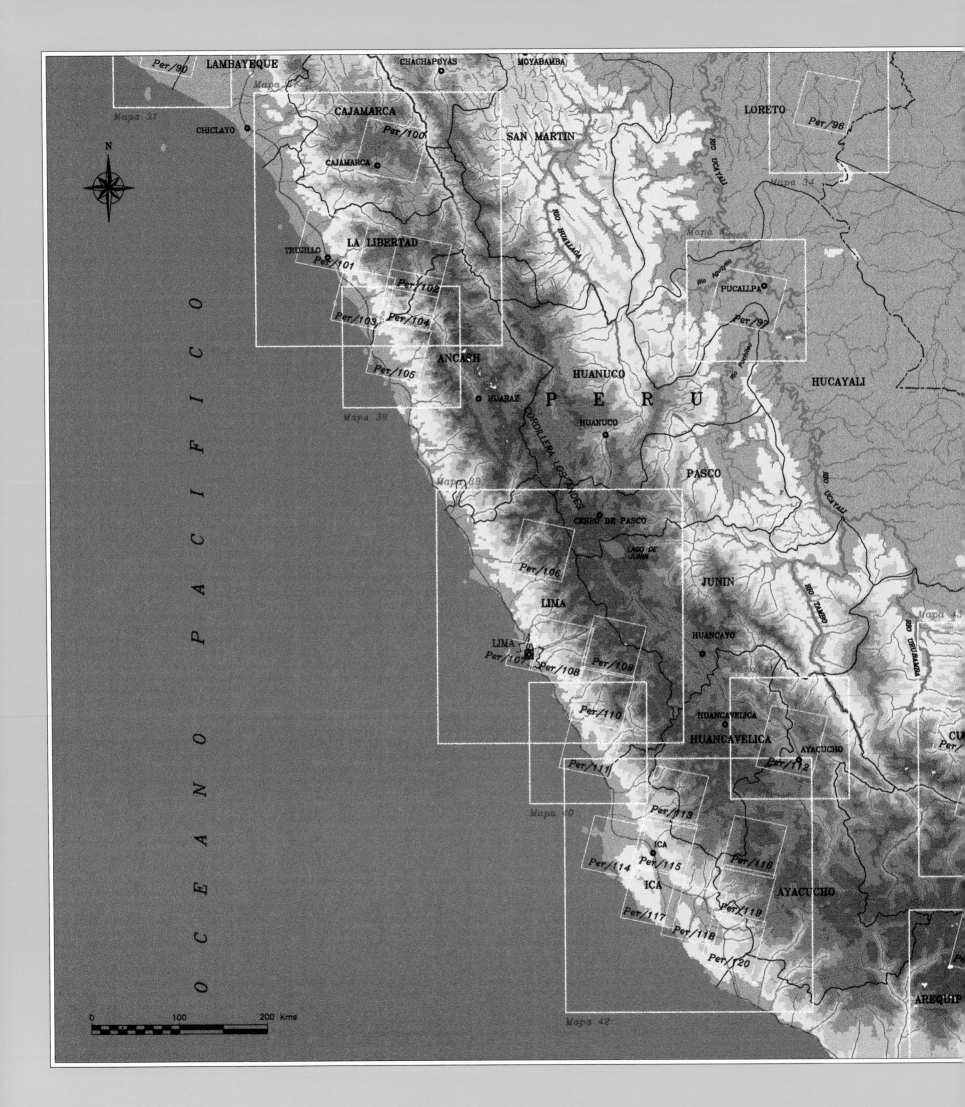

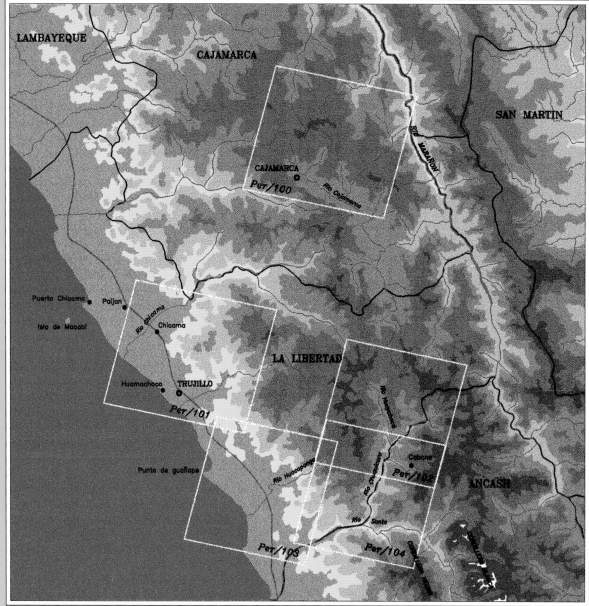

Map 37

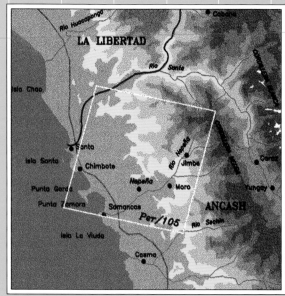

Map 38

Per/100. *Region in the northern Peruvian Andes, over 3,000 m. above sea level, in the province of Cajamarca.*

This region, deep in the Andes, is traditionally known as Cajamarca and inhabited by Indians who live off elementary agricultural activities on unfertile steppes. The city of Cajamarca is where Pizarro's soldiers threw the Inca Atahualpa into captivity.

**Per/101. *City of Trujillo in northern Peru's coastal desert. Province of Lambayeque.*
Page 172.**

One notes the difference in colour between the grey and white sands of the coastal desert of "La Chala", the irrigated agricultural cone of the Chicama river to the north and the Chuquicara flowing through the city of Trujillo. Mastery of hydraulic techniques have permitted human settlement in the zone since very ancient times: the city was formerly Chanchán, capital of the pre-Inca empire of Chimú. Trujillo, with a population of around 200,000, lies midway between Lima and the northern reaches of the coastal desert, which makes it a regional capital.

Per/102. *Northern zone of the Peruvian Andes in the region of Cabana.*

These highlands deep in the Andes, traditionally inhabited by Indians, are a desperately poor part of the country, and a copper and iron mining zone. Along the tributaries of the Chuquicara river, which flows down to Trujillo on the coastline, a few small and poor villages were settled, the most important of which is Cabana. The "bronze" or metallic aspect of the slopes stems from the peculiar reflection of light on bare walls of rock. The mountains of bare rock belong to the Cordillera Negra, and the higher, snow-covered mountains to the Cordillera Blanca.

Per/103. *Desert region in northern Peru's Pacific coast, between Lima and the frontier with Ecuador.* **Page 170.**

This zone is situated in the proximity of Trujillo. In a totally desert environment, mastery of irrigation techniques allows to transform the estuaries of rivers flowing down from the cordillera into agricultural oases which produce corn, vegetables, cassava and rice. This can be observed clearly on the river cones, where irrigated fields appear as red carpets.

Per/104. *Immense slopes of the Peruvian Cordillera and Chuquicara river.* **Page 171.**

From time immemorial, this zone has been inhabited by an Indian population. The Chuquicara river makes possible the existence of oases on the coast and small watersheds along its course, with a traditional subsistence agriculture of corn and potato. In contrast to the coast, the inland presents conditions unfavourable to development. A parallel copper-mining activity allows a small population to remain in these areas.

Per/105. *City of Chimbote in northern Peru's Pacific coast desert.* **Page 173.**

One observes agricultural activity on the rivers, beside the urban centre of Chimbote. Also noteworthy is the local anchovy fishing industry, the world's largest, with processed derivatives such as fishmeal. Apart from irrigation, the rivers provide hydroelectric power to the towns of Chimbote and, further north, Trujillo. Despite is inhospitable, forbidding aspect, the coastal plains are largely inhabited, with five cities of over 200,000 people: Arequipa, Trujillo, Piura, Chimbote and Chiclayo, which, with the inclusion of Lima, gather more than half the country's population.

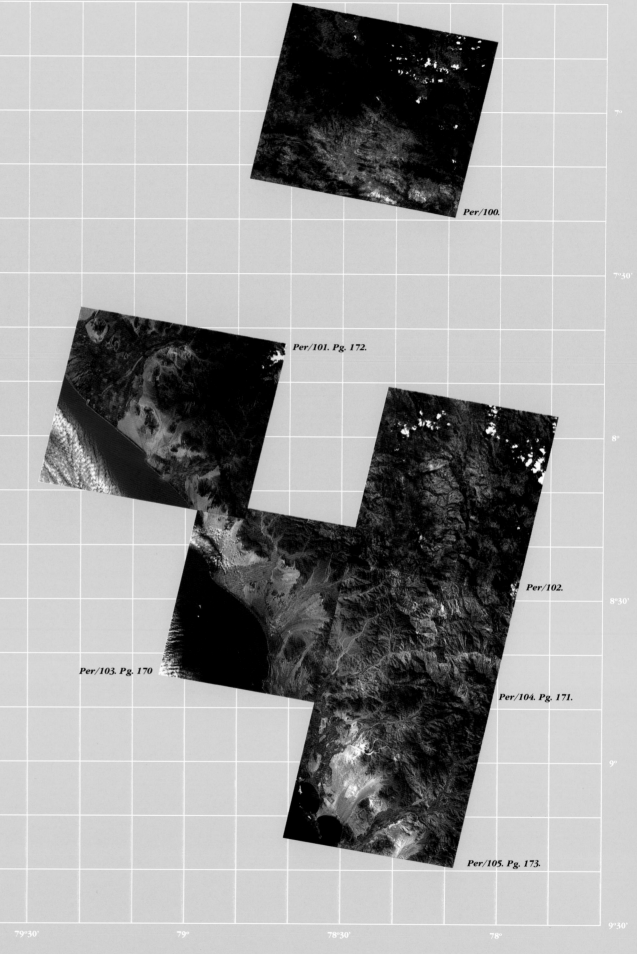

Per/100.

Per/101. Pg. 172.

Per/102.

Per/103. Pg. 170

Per/104. Pg. 171.

Per/105. Pg. 173.

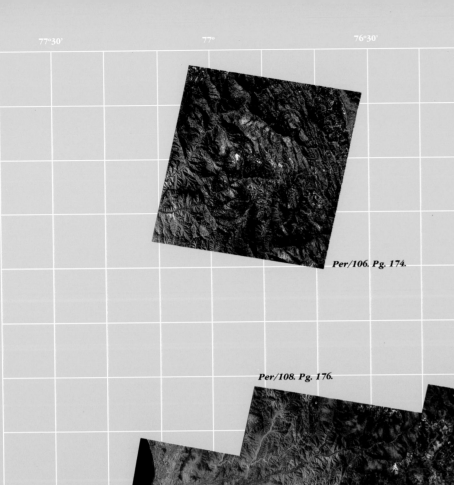

Per/106. Pg. 174.

Per/108. Pg. 176.

Per/107. Pg. 175.

Per/109.

Per/110.

Per/111. Pg. 177.

Per/107. *Lima, the Peruvian capital, on the Pacific coast. Province of Lima.* Page 175.

Lima was founded by Francisco Pizarro in 1535, and today its population is over eight million people. Its geographical configuration resembles that of the towns on the coastal desert to the north. San Lorenzo island faces the bay of Lima and offers ships a natural shelter against Pacific gales. Between ocean and Andes, at the estuary of three rivers, the course of which appears conspicuously in red, the city occupies the entire alluvial cone of the Rímac in the centre, and a good part of the alluvial cone of the Chillón, to the north. In the grey heart of the city, one notes the historical centre, with its chessboard pattern, from where the major arteries, which enabled the capital's modern development, lead to the coast. Housing areas along these thoroughfares show in dark grey. The red blots of parks and gardens indicate upper-class districts, whereas the more widespread pale grey areas correspond mostly to *barriadas,* built-up from former shanty-towns, north of the Rímac, to the city's south-east.

Per/108. *Foothills of the Andean Cordillera and industrial zone near Lima.* Page 176.

The level terrain is occupied by industries, and river basins by farmlands which supply Lima with fruits and vegetables. The almost total absence of human settlements in the mountain area underlines the capital's voracious population concentration.

Per/109. *High mountains in Peru's interior, on the latitude of Lima, with snowy peaks of the Cordillera Blanca.*

The snowy peaks are encircled by glacial lakes, which appear in black in the picture, whereas mountains show in red, because of vegetation on their lower slopes. Human presence is scarce, mostly miners struggling, in arduous conditions, to exploit the various metal deposits.

Per/106. *Peru's Andean Cordillera in the province of San Martín.* Page 174.

This zone of immense slopes of the cordillera, between 2,000 and 3,000 m. above sea level, is a traditional Indian habitat. The rivers flowing down its gorges are the lifeblood of the coastal oases. The region is rich in iron and copper, but there are no significant urban concentrations.

162

Per/110. *Snowy peaks of Peru's Andean Cordillera, to the south-east of Lima.*

One can distinguish several geographic environments in this picture. To the north-east, snowy peaks appearing in white, and slopes denuded by erosion due to local mining activities, where rock shows in yellow or white. These high expanses are separated by deep valleys, with inclines appearing in red because of forest vegetation, and with little black spots or streaks revealing glacial lakes. To the south-west, mountain slopes of lesser altitude show in a bronze colour.

Per/111. *Desert of "La Chala" on Peru's Pacific coast, in the province of Ica.* **Page 177.**

In this picture, one can observe the oasis of Cañete, with its extensive fruit orchards and vineyards. Around 100,000 people live off the local agriculture. Cañete is famous for its wine, and especially for its distillation of pisco, Peru's national firewater. The mosaic of red hues is characteristic of this part of the coast.

Per/112. *Outskirts of the city of Ayacucho in the Peruvian Andes.* **Page 12.**

This is an extremely poor zone, which only manages to survive thanks to lead and silver mining, cattle raising and subsistence agriculture. The majority of the population is Indian or *mestizo*. The city of Ayacucho appears in the eastern part of the picture.

Per/112. Pg. 12.

Map 39

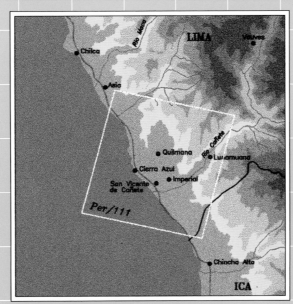

Map 40

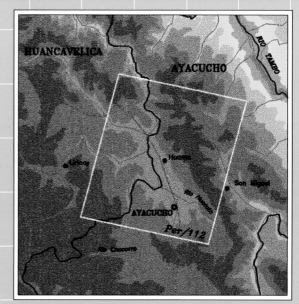

Map 41

163

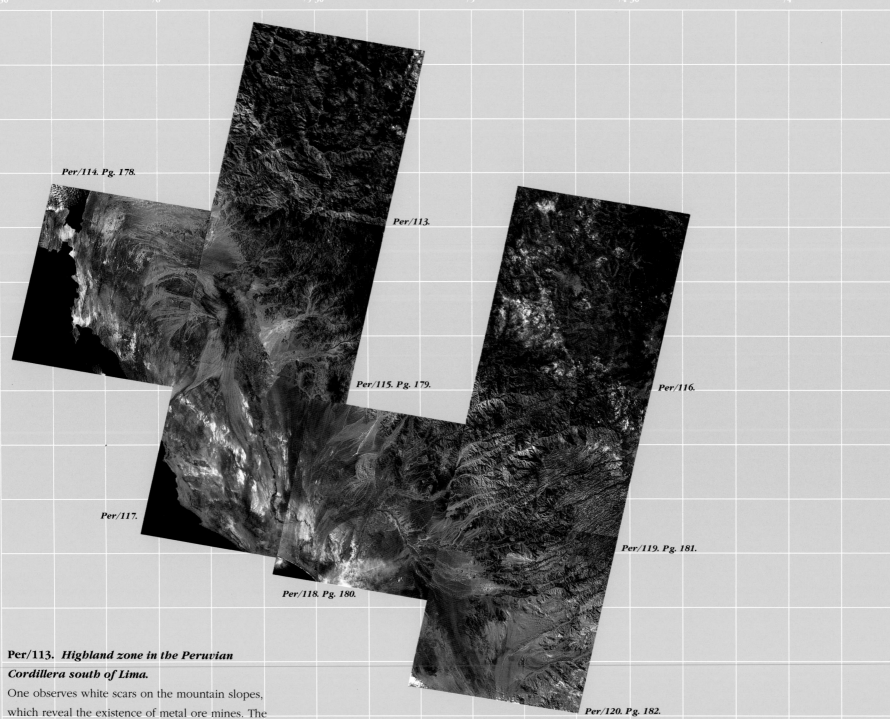

Per/114. Pg. 178.

Per/113.

Per/115. Pg. 179.

Per/116.

Per/117.

Per/119. Pg. 181.

Per/118. Pg. 180.

Per/120. Pg. 182.

Per/113. Highland zone in the Peruvian Cordillera south of Lima.

One observes white scars on the mountain slopes, which reveal the existence of metal ore mines. The centre of the picture is crossed by the Chiris river, which flows through the town of Huancayo and the upper valley of which appears in red. The road, coming from the northern mining area, passes through the valley, an important communication route towards the coast. In this steep mountain environment, riverbanks are the only places suitable for human settlement. The same occurs further north, on the visible stretch of the San Juan river.

Per/114. Desert of "La Chala" on Peru's Pacific coast, in the province of Arequipa. Page 178.

On the bay to the north of the picture, appears the town of Pisco, which gave its name to Peru's traditional firewater, distilled from local grapes. To the south lies the Bahía de la Independencia, with the island of the same name. The region is extremely dry, and farmlands scarce. The green corollas at the centre of the picture are traces of the alluvial cones of dried-up riverbeds.

Per/115. Intensive agriculture on the banks of the Ica river, on Peru's Pacific coast. Page 179.

The zone's considerable agricultural activity has prospered thanks to the Ica river. The town of the same name lies almost at the foot of the Andes. Local produce, sugarcane, rice, cotton, fruit and vegetables, supplies Lima's markets and food-processing industries.

Per/116. _Mountain zone deep in the southern Peruvian Andes, with snowy peaks of almost 6,000 m._

The glacial-type relief is emphasized by the presence of deep lakes and valleys, and by the relatively scarce vegetation. This is a zone of vertiginous rocky precipices, which conspires with the freezing climate to discourage human presence. Snow-fed fountainheads give birth to rivers flowing down eastwards.

Per/117. _Desert of "La Chala" on Peru's Pacific coast, with intensively cultivated oases._

The Ica river, flowing north to south, etches a red streak in a monotonous landscape of sand and ash. Symptoms of erosion are evident: dried-out riverbeds, wind-shaped sand dunes… and roads. To the north, near the town of Ica, irrigated fields show as red strips: sugarcane, rice, cotton, fruit and vegetables are grown, which supply Lima's markets and food-processing industries.

Per/118. _Desert of "La Chala" on Peru's Pacific coast, in the province of Arequipa._ Page 180.

One remarks the intensively cultivated oases on the banks of rivers flowing down from the cordillera. Along the Ingenio river grows agricultural produce which provides the local food-processing industry. The town of Nazca, with its iron deposits, lies a little further to the south-east, and enjoys regional importance. The bleakness of the landscape sets out rectilinear roads and effects of water and wind erosion: sedimentary build-ups, undulating dune hills and seasonal riverbeds.

Per/119. _The Peruvian Andes east of Nazca. Province of Arequipa._ Page 181.

The mountainous part of the picture lacks signs of human presence, explainable by the discouraging barrenness. Nevertheless, as a natural water reservoir, it proves useful by feeding the oasis farmlands of "La Chala". Some of the foothills are rich in iron, especially to the south-east of the picture, near the town of Nazca. One can discern the contour lines and impact of river erosion on the slopes.

Per/120. _Transition zone between desert and Cordillera foothills, in the Peruvian province of Arequipa._ Page 182.

In contrast to Peru's northern coast, the shoreline south of Lima is sparsely populated. Human presence is concentrated in oases, where irrigation permits either subsistence or export-oriented agriculture, or in iron and copper mining areas. This region south of Nazca exports its iron ore through the harbour of San Juan, to the west.

Map 42

Per/121. *Gorge of the Urubamba river in the Peruvian Andes east of the Amazon jungle. Province of Cuzco.* **Page 187.**

On these highlands at over 3,000 m. above sea level, known as "El Piso Quechua", lies the source of the Urubamba river. As observed in the southern part of the picture, the Urubamba originates in Cuzco's inner valley, where it receives two tributaries. It follows its course to the north, passing through the town of Quillabamba, until its confluence with the Lares, which flows from the east, after which its course switches westwards. These narrow, almost secretive valleys mark the transition between Andean cultures and jungle frontiers, through the Urubamba, gateway to Peru's *Oriente*.

Per/122. *Region of the deep Peruvian Andes known as "Piso Quechua". Province of Cuzco.* **Page 186.**

In a valley spreading between the Apurímac river to the south and Urubamba to the north, Cuzco ("navel of the world", in Quechua), ancient capital of the Inca empire, is situated 75 km. south-east of the lost city of Macchu Picchu. Little remains of its past splendour, laid waste by the Spaniards. Today, the region's growth lags behind the rest of Peru. Nevertheless, a privileged location, close to two major rivers and endless valleys, assures its agricultural autonomy, thanks to corn and sheep and llamas. And Cuzco retains some of its past glory as perennial capital of the highlands, in its traditional arrogance letting Lima rule over the coastline. The Urubamba river corridor to the Amazon jungles makes it a gateway to the new frontiers of colonization. In a nutshell, Cuzco represents a shrine of Inca history, and at the same time a regional starting point for Peruvian development eastwards to the Amazon.

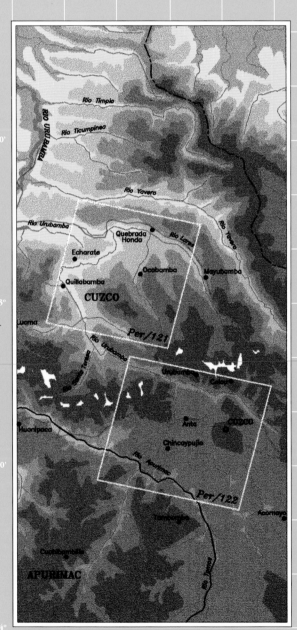

Map 43

Per/121. Pg. 187.

Per/122. Pg. 186.

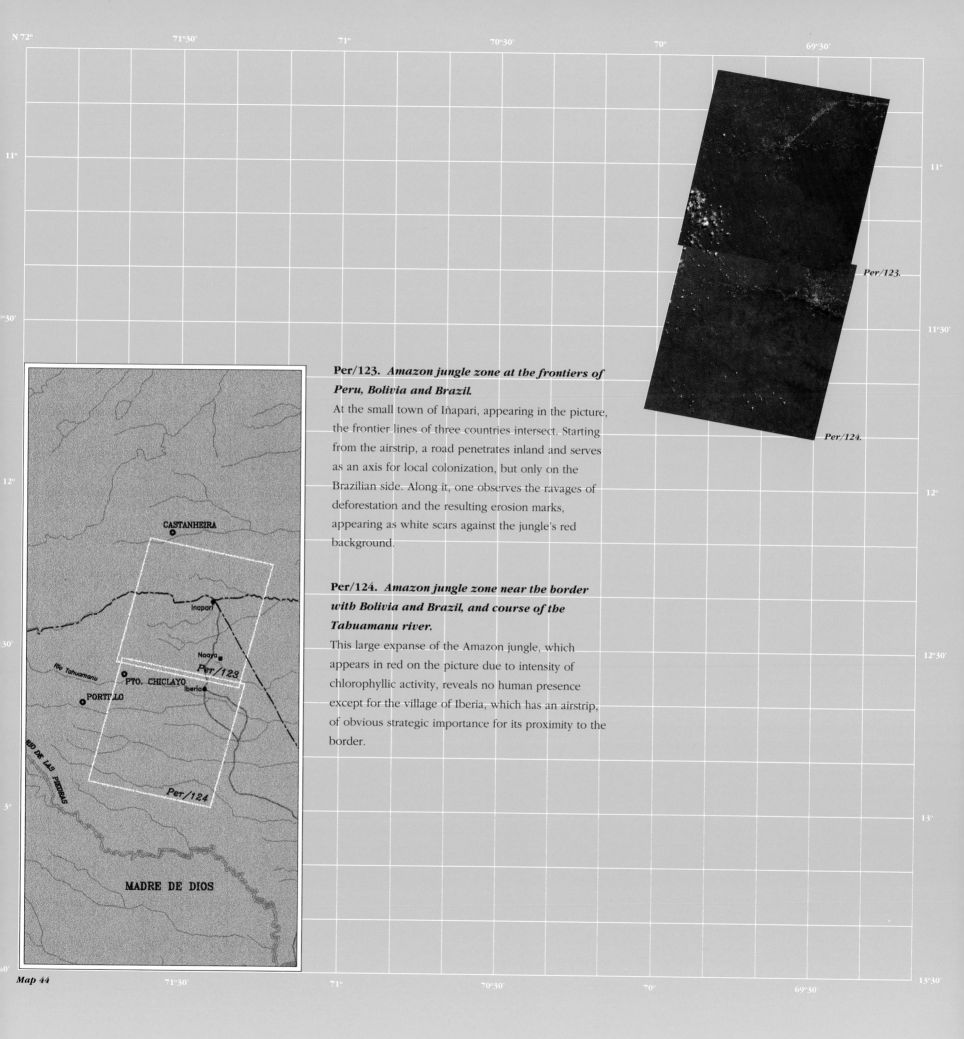

Per/123. *Amazon jungle zone at the frontiers of Peru, Bolivia and Brazil.*
At the small town of Iñapari, appearing in the picture, the frontier lines of three countries intersect. Starting from the airstrip, a road penetrates inland and serves as an axis for local colonization, but only on the Brazilian side. Along it, one observes the ravages of deforestation and the resulting erosion marks, appearing as white scars against the jungle's red background.

Per/124. *Amazon jungle zone near the border with Bolivia and Brazil, and course of the Tahuamanu river.*
This large expanse of the Amazon jungle, which appears in red on the picture due to intensity of chlorophyllic activity, reveals no human presence except for the village of Iberia, which has an airstrip, of obvious strategic importance for its proximity to the border.

Per/123.

Per/124.

CASTANHEIRA

Iñapari

Noaya

Per/123

Rio Tahuamanu

PTO. CHICLAYO

Iberia

PORTILLO

RIO DE LAS PIEDRAS

Per/124

MADRE DE DIOS

Map 44

Bol/125. Pg. 188.

Bol/125. *Confluence of the Beni and Madre de Dios rivers in north-eastern Bolivia's tropical rain forest.* Page 188.

To the east, a little before the frontier with Brazil, the Beni river, flowing south-to-north, meets up with the Madre de Dios. Further north, the Ortón pours into the Beni. All these rivers follow extremely erratic courses, with many "dead" meanders and dried-up beds. The Beni flows into the Madeira, on Brazilian territory, and thus represents Bolivia's gateway to the Amazon. The town of Riberalta, almost on the confluence of the three rivers, lives off its commercial relations with Brazil, rubber plantations and timbering.

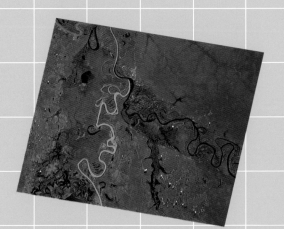

Bol/126. Pg. 189.

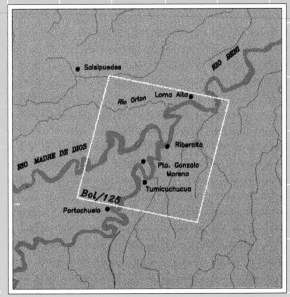

Map 45

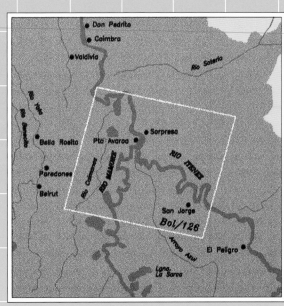

Map 46

Bol/126. *Frontier between Bolivia and Brazil at the confluence of the Mamoré and Iténez rivers.* Page 189.

One can observe the erratic and meandering course of the rivers, characterized by large volume, slow current and malleable sandbanks. Human presence can be detected by fires scattered around the small town of Surprêsa, on the Brazilian side of the Iténez river. Local activity is reduced to lumbering and rubber-tapping.

Bra/127. Pg. 191.

Bra/128. Pg. 190.

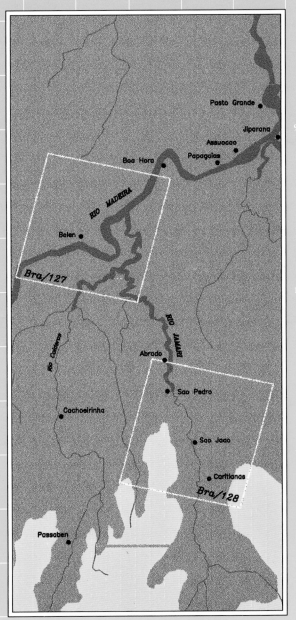
Map 47

Bra/127. *Marshy curve of the Madeira river in the Brazilian Amazon jungle.* **Page 191.**

A little eastward of this curve of the Madeira, one observes the confluence of its black waters with the blue waters of the Jamarí. On the left side of the latter, a tributary appears, the Candeias, coming from the south. All these lethargic rivers feed the lakes and marshlands typical of the region. The small town of Jamarí, on its namesake river, is surrounded by large fields showing evidence of fruit or rice agro-industries. Further west, one notes the agricultural outskirts of Pôrto Velho, on the Madeira river

Bra/128. *Course of the Jamarí river, a tributary of the Madeira, in the Brazilian Amazon jungle. State of Rondonia.* **Page 190.**

The small town of São Pedro, near a bend of the Jamarí river, is the zone's trading centre. This is a territory of organized colonization, with roads perpendicular to the river penetrating deep into the jungle. With its unchecked methods of deforestation, this type of "penetrative" colonization, needless to say, is highly detrimental to the jungle. Clearings are planted with rice, cassava and fruit.

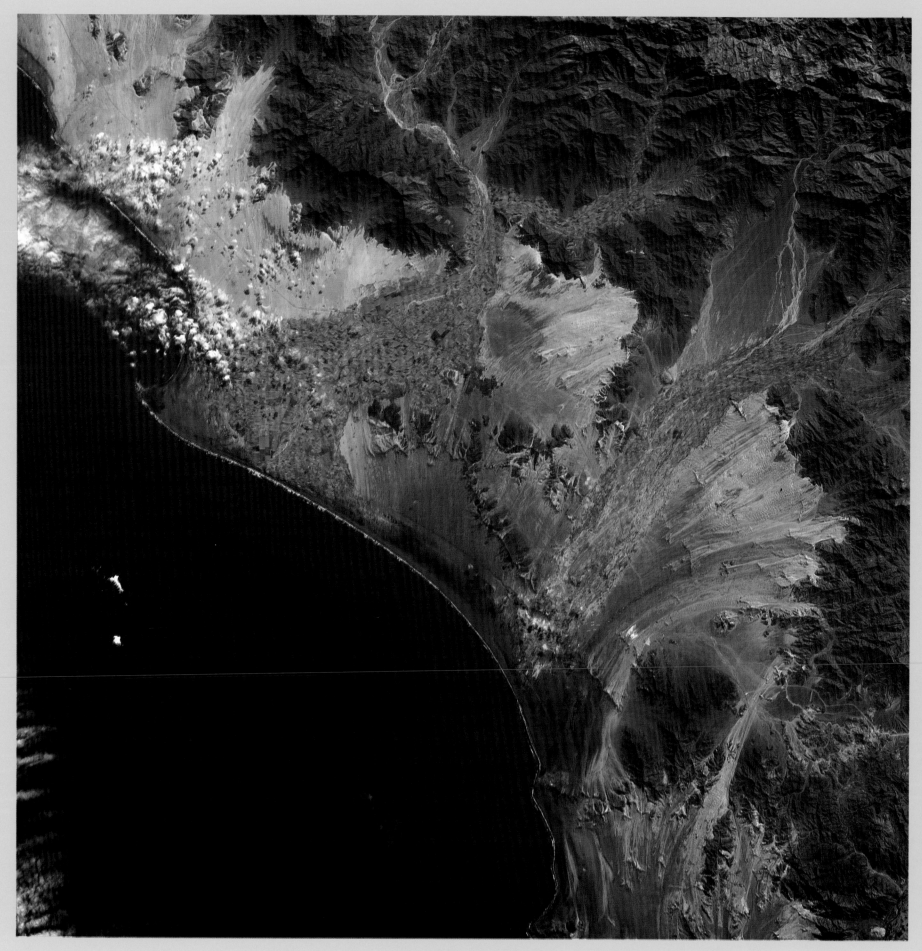

Desert region in northern Peru's Pacific coast,
between Lima and the frontier with Ecuador.

Per/103, page 161

Immense slopes of the Peruvian Cordillera
and Chuquicara river.

Per/104, page 161

City of Trujillo in northern Peru's coast desert.
Province of Lambayeque.

Per/101, page 161

City of Chimbote in northern Peru's
Pacific coast desert.

Per/105, page 161

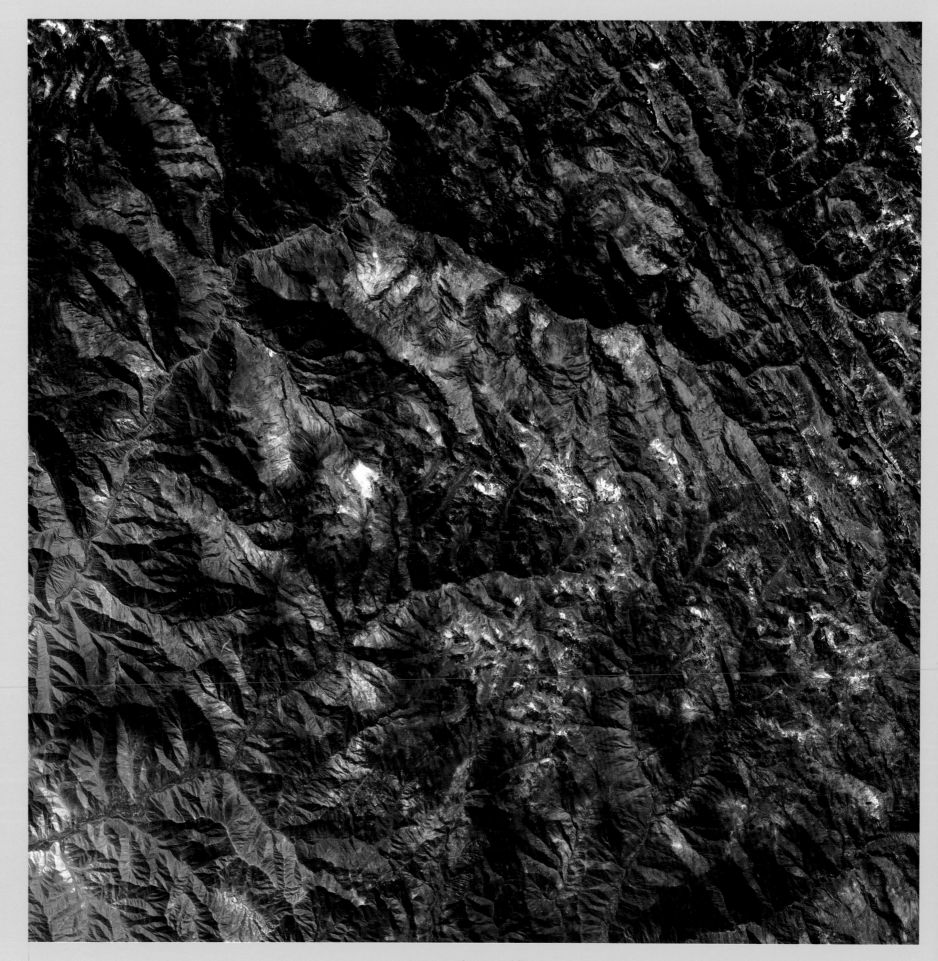

*Peru's Andean Cordillera
in the province of San Martín.*

Per/106, page 162

*Lima, the Peruvian capital,
on the Pacific coast. Province of Lima.*

Per/107, page 162

Foothills of the Andean Cordillera
and industrial zone near Lima.

Per/108, page 162

Desert of "La Chala" on Peru's Pacific coast,
in the province of Ica.

Per/111, page 162

Desert of "La Chala" on Peru's Pacific coast,
in the province of Arequipa.

Per/114, page 164

Intensive agriculture on the banks of the Ica river,
on Peru's Pacific coast.

Per/115, page 164

Desert of "La Chala" on Peru's Pacific coast,
in the province of Arequipa.

Per/118, page 164.

The Peruvian Andes east of Nazca.
Province of Arequipa.

Per/119, page 164

*Transition zone between desert and Cordillera foothills,
in the Peruvian province of Arequipa.*

Per/120, page 164

Beginnings of the snowcapped Cordillera de Huanzo deep
in the Peruvian Andes. Province of Arequipa.

Per/129, page 194

*Cordillera de Huanzo and Ampato snowcap
in the Peruvian province of Puno.*

Per/130, page 194

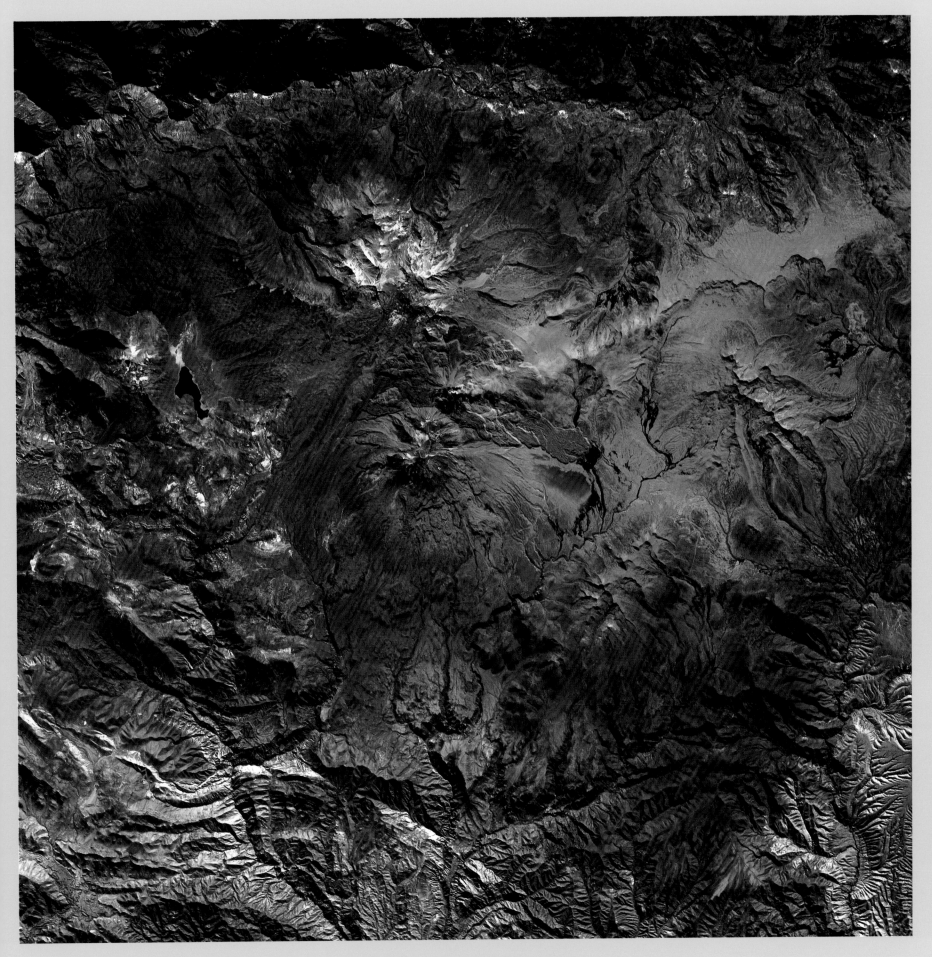

*Cordillera de Huanzo, Cordillera Real
and Ampato snowcap, in the Peruvian Andes.*

Per/131, page 194

Region of the deep Peruvian Andes known as "Piso Quechua".
Province of Cuzco.

Per/122, page 166

*Gorge of the Urubamba river in the Peruvian Andes east
of the Amazon jungle. Province of Cuzco.*

Per/121, page 166

*Confluence of the Beni and Madre de Dios rivers
in north-eastern Bolivia's tropical rain forest.*

Bol/125, page 168

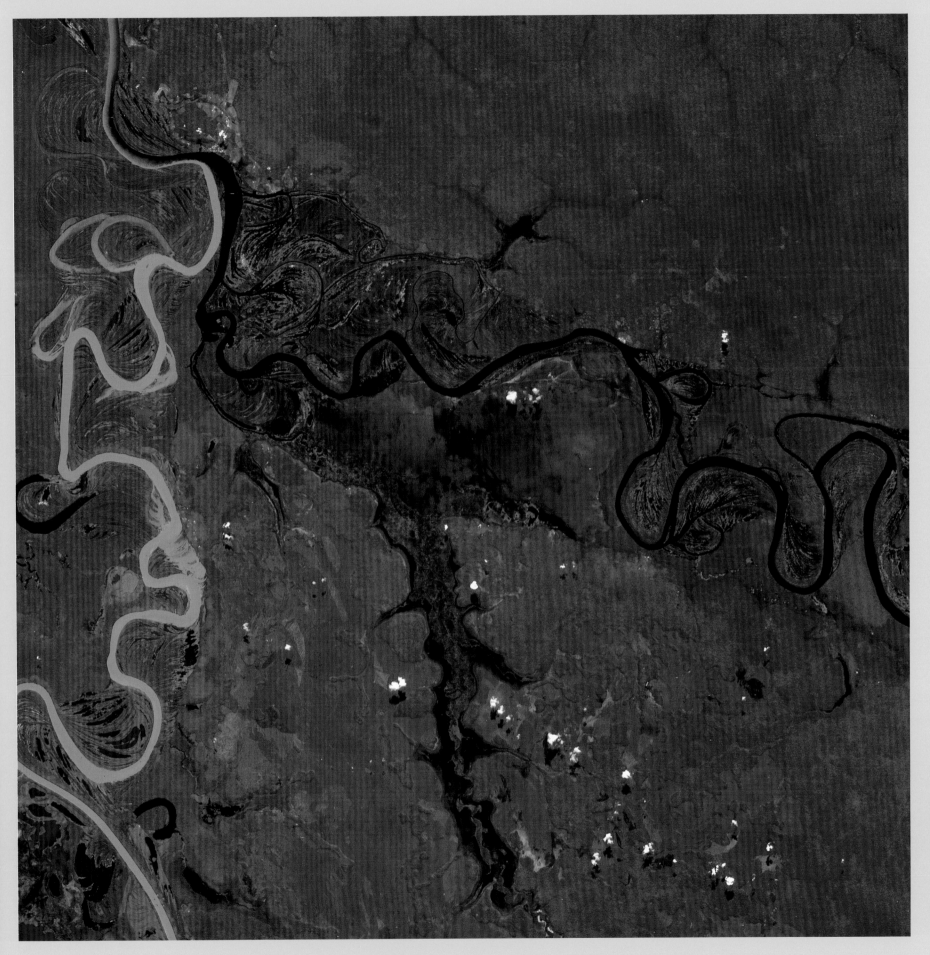

*Frontier between Bolivia and Brazil
at the confluence of the Mamoré and Iténez rivers.*

Bol/126, page 168

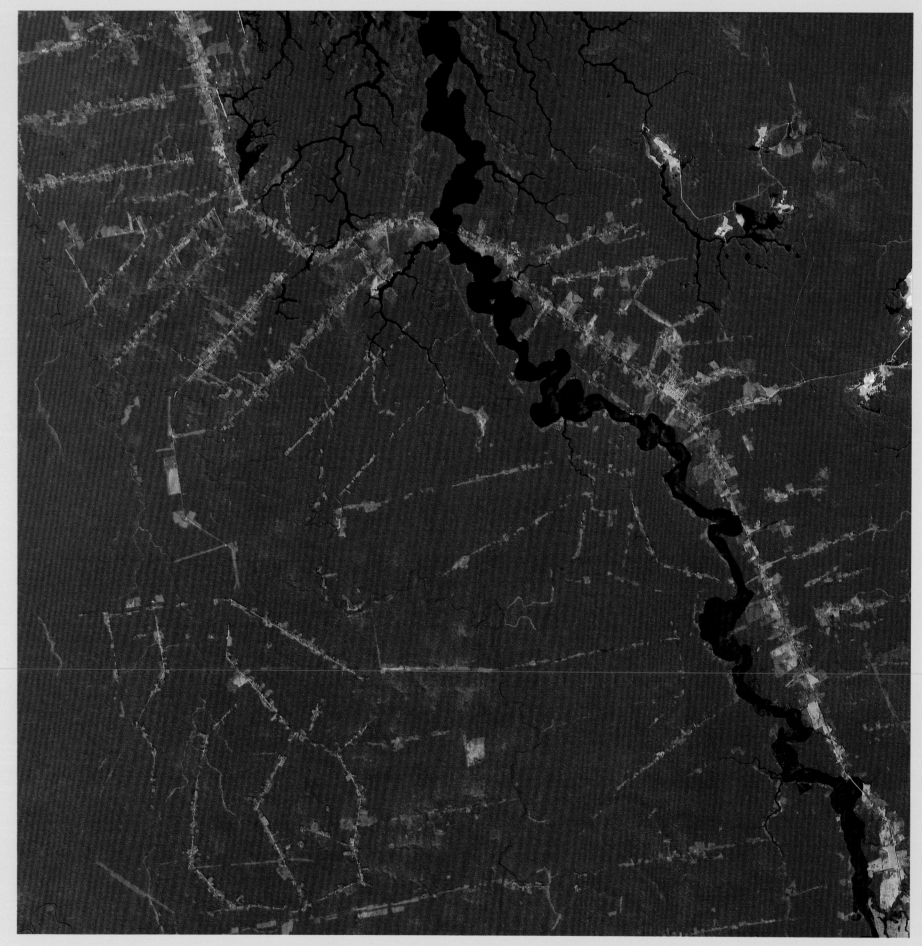

Course of the Jamarí river, a tributary of the Madeira,
in the Brazilian Amazon jungle. State of Rondonia.

Bra/128, page 169

*Marshy curve of the Madeira river
in the Brazilian Amazon jungle.*

Bra/127, page 169

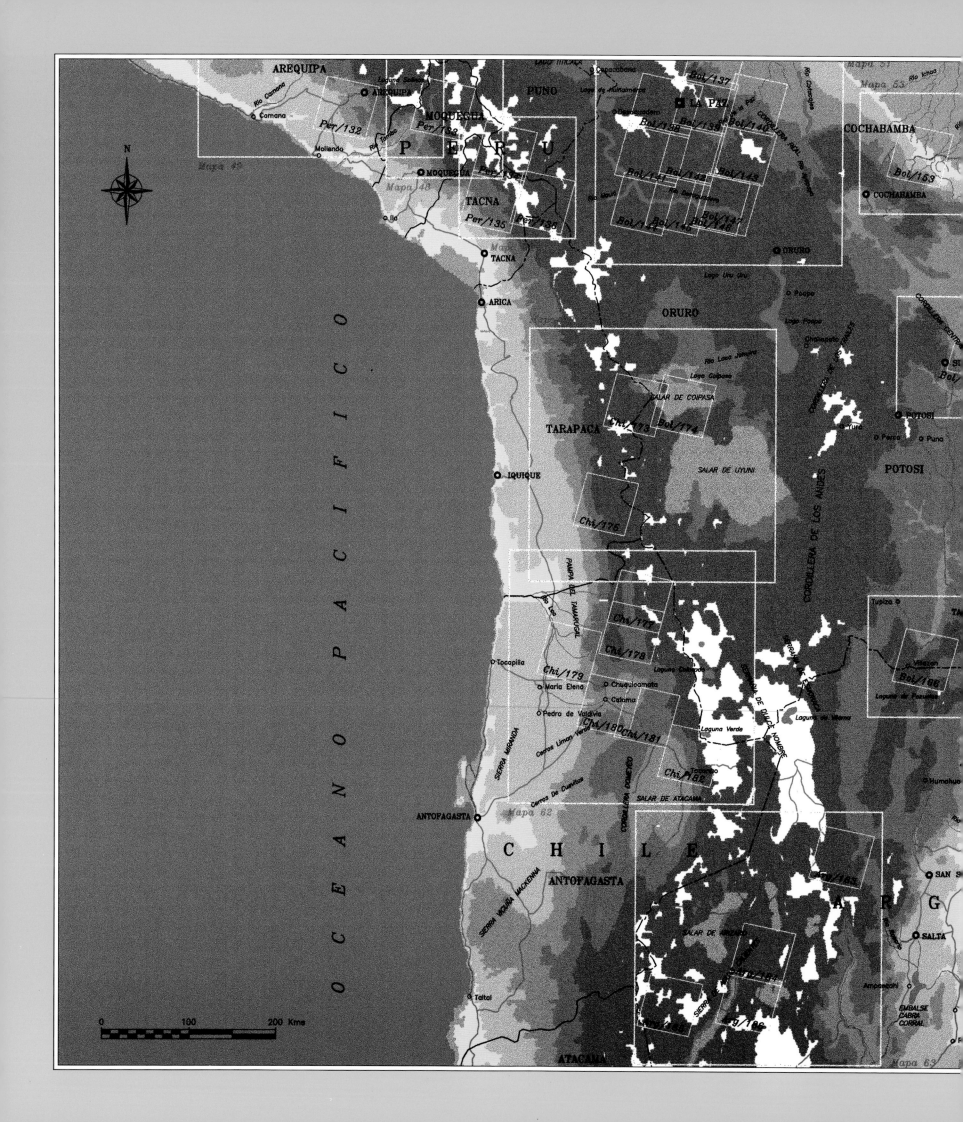

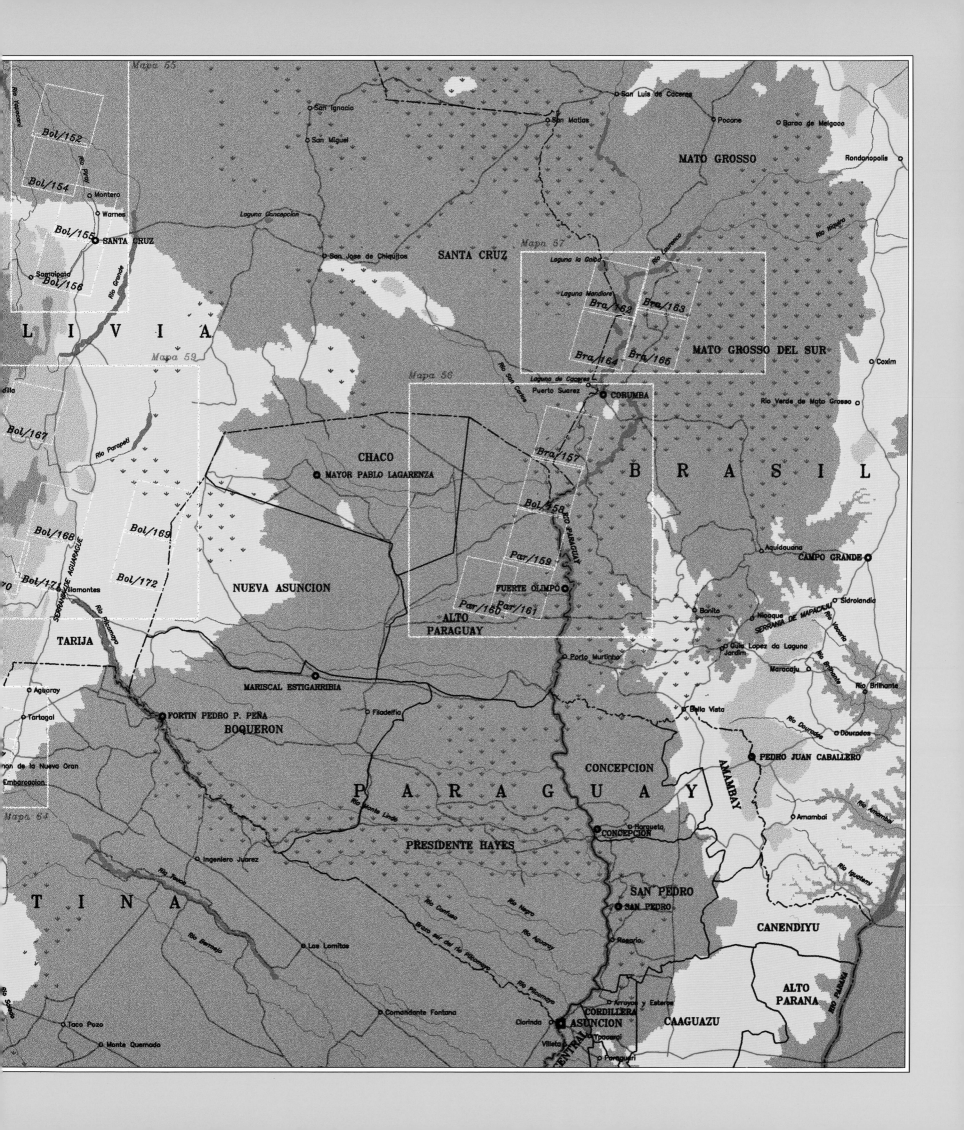

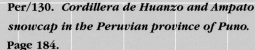

Per/129. Pg. 183.

Per/130. Pg. 184.

Per/131. Pg. 185.

Per/130. *Cordillera de Huanzo and Ampato snowcap in the Peruvian province of Puno.* **Page 184.**

The zone belongs to the Cordillera Real, with the snowy peaks of the Ampato, in the south-eastern part of the picture, at 6,300 m. above sea level. The mountain's entire northern flank is eroded by a river which springs at an altitude of 3,000 m. Its course enables communication between the coast and the interior of the country, as far as Lake Titicaca.

Per/132. *Desert region of "La Chala", in south-western Peru. Province of Arequipa.* **Page 210.**

The zone is composed of coastal deserts and oases, on a slope of almost 2,000 m. which sweeps down from Arequipa, to the north-east, to the sea. The prevailing colour is grey, which corresponds to rock and sand, and the red streaks are cultivated areas. One notes human presence by the airfields of Arequipa to the north-east, Vitor in the centre, surrounded by red farmlands, and Mariano Velgar to the south. One sees several irrigated fields in the form of red and yellow squares. The straight line is the railway linking the Pacific coast to the Amazon province of Madre de Dios.

Per/133. *The Peruvian Andes south-east of Arequipa. Province of Moquegua.* **Page 211.**

The zone's highest summits reach an altitude of over 5,000 m. The Tambo river winds through the volcanic slopes of the snow-covered mountains before continuing towards the coast. The grey colour of the slopes denotes volcanic rock and massive quantities of ash. The yellow colour could be sulphur near the approaches of the snow-covered range, which have minimal volcanic activity.

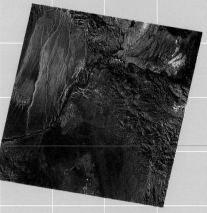

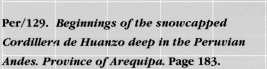

Per/132. Pg. 210.

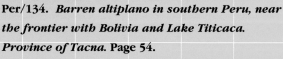

Per/133. Pg. 211.

Per/129. *Beginnings of the snowcapped Cordillera de Huanzo deep in the Peruvian Andes. Province of Arequipa.* **Page 183.**

The zone belongs to the Cordillera Real, where the tallest peak, the snow-capped Coropuna, soars to over 6,400 m. One observes the aridity of the slopes, the high-altitude glacial lakes, and the white pinnacles covered in perpetual snows starting at 5,000 m. Due to the altitude and desolation, there's no human presence throughout the entire zone. One only notes a few roads crossing the massif.

Per/131. *Cordillera de Huanzo, Cordillera Real and Ampato snowcap, in the Peruvian Andes.* **Page 185.**

In contrast to the previous picture, Per/130, this picture, taken a year later, shows vastly-reduced snowcaps. The considerable thaw is due to various factors. One of them can be examined in the picture: whirls of smoke indicating an increase in volcanic activity, which, by heating the surface, provokes the thawing of the upper layers.

Per/134. *Barren altiplano in southern Peru, near the frontier with Bolivia and Lake Titicaca. Province of Tacna.* **Page 54.**

In an extraordinary lunar landscape, characterized by yellow, black, ochre and white colours, one observes the lakes of Villacota and Viscacha, formed by the seasonal thawing of surface snows. This panorama, owing to its particular climate and local volcanic activity, gathers over a relatively small area the strangest colours observable in nature.

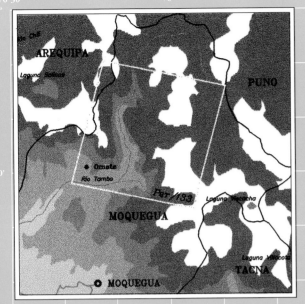

Map 48

Per/135. *The Cordillera in southern Peru near the border with Chile, in the province of Tacna.* Page 212.

In this zone rich in copper, one discerns the village of Estique, in the middle of the red patch. To the northwest of the picture, the small lake of Aricota shows as a black spot. In the southern part, volcanic formation and distinctive erosion have shaped a barren, tabular meseta.

Per/134. Pg. 54.

Per/135. Pg. 212.

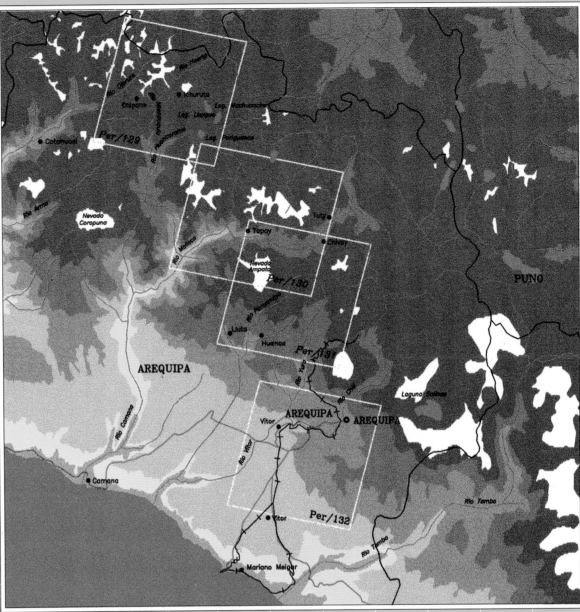

Map 49

Per/136. *Peruvian border zone, north of Chile and west of Bolivia.* Page 213.

The blue expanse in the centre of the picture corresponds to Laguna Blanca. Green-grey denotes the type of sand and ash of surrounding terrain.

Per/136. Pg. 213.

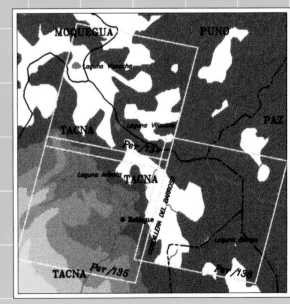

Map 50

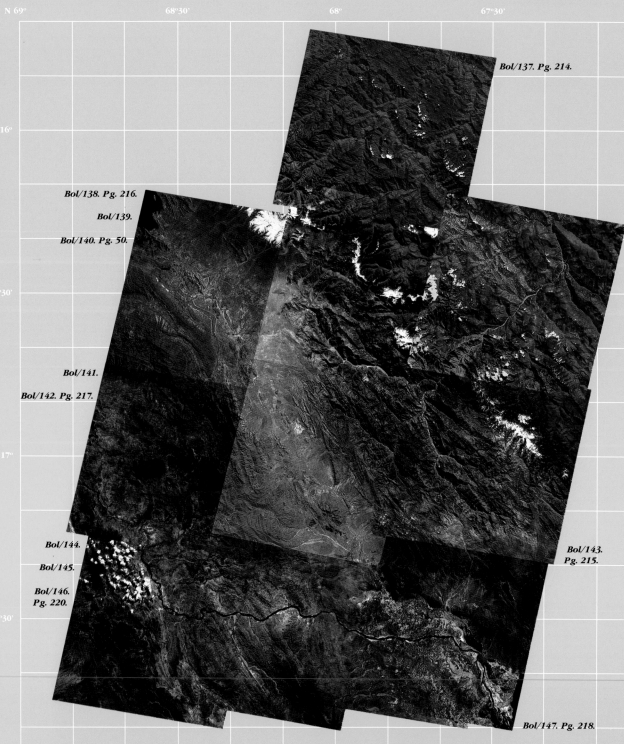

Bol/137. Pg. 214.

Bol/138. Pg. 216.

Bol/139.

Bol/140. Pg. 50.

Bol/141.

Bol/142. Pg. 217.

Bol/144.

Bol/145.

Bol/146. Pg. 220.

Bol/143. Pg. 215.

Bol/147. Pg. 218.

Bol/139. *The city of La Paz, administrative capital of Bolivia, leaning against the Cordillera Real.*

In the picture, one observes how the city extends over several echelons down from the jagged gorge of the Choqueyapu river, near the international airport, on a meseta 4,200 m. above sea level. To the east, behind the cordillera, one distinguishes the tropical valleys of the *Yungas*.

Bol/140. *The Cordillera Real, east of La Paz, where the tributaries of the eastern jungle rivers spring. Province of La Paz.* **Page 50.**

Deserted in higher stretches, because of the freezing climate and unproductive soil, and because practically all the local population is concentrated in La Paz, the mountain becomes more hospitable downstream with the appearance of tropical vegetation. Irrigation, supplied by rivers from the glaciers, favours agricultural prosperity in the *Yungas*.

Bol/141. *Desolate Puna region on the Bolivian altiplano, communication route between La Paz and Oruro.*

This zone is sparsely inhabited. Tin, today a commodity of piddling value, was formerly transported by truck and railway over its forbidding expanses. One observes the arid and steep relief of the mountain slopes, with oases downhill and along the roads. To the south appears the Desaguadero river.

Bol/142. *The Cordillera Real and the dry Puna plateau which stretches between La Paz and Oruro.* **Page 217.**

Whereas the mountains show no sign of human life, on the altiplano below one observes the straight lines of the railway and road, which link La Paz to the old mining city of Oruro, which, for over a century, owed its growth to tin.

Bol/143. *Dry altiplano and snowcapped mountain range in the central area of Bolivia's Cordillera Real.* **Page 215.**

The "bronze" colour of the mountains reveals the zone's relative bleakness. Human presence is practically nil, except for the roads which cross the cordillera transversely.

Bol/137. *Eastern foothills of the Bolivian Cordillera, the colossal Illampú and the town of Caranavi.* **Page 214.**

One can observe the course of the Coroico river, a tributary of the Beni, which springs to the east of the cordillera and flows through the small town of Caranavi, a gateway for colonization of the north-eastern tropical zones. These torrid valleys, known as *Yungas,* provide corn, fruit, vegetables, coffee and coca leaves to La Paz.

Bol/138. *The snow-capped peaks of the Illimani, which tower over the city of La Paz, the Bolivian administrative capital.* **Page 216.**

Because of its altitude, the zone is extremely dry, as indicated in the picture by green with yellow striations, which correspond to bare rock. La Paz spreads at various levels: the "balcony" of El Alto, with its lower-class suburbs and international airport, at 4,200 m. above sea level; the historical centre, at 3,600 m.; and the residential districts, below 3,500 m.

Bol/148. Pg. 45.

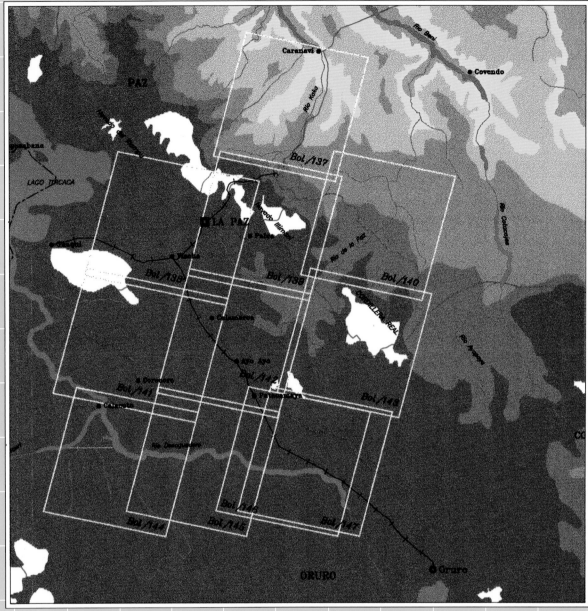

Map 51

Bol/144. *Course of the Desaguadero river on the subdesert Puna of the Bolivian altiplano.*

In the north-western part of the picture, one notes the course of the Desaguadero river and its confluence with the Mauri. On this confluence lies the tiny town of Calacoto, an oasis thanks to river water, in the midst of the surrounding bleakness. The zone's strategic importance is due to the proximity of the frontiers with Peru and Chile, to which Bolivia relinquished its access to the sea after a disastrous war.

Bol/145. *Aymara Indian territory on the Bolivian altiplano south of La Paz.*

The Desaguadero river, which flows from Lake Poopó to Lake Titicaca, flows through this zone characterized by extremely severe living conditions, due to its outlandish desolation and altitude, over 4,000 m. above sea level. This is one of the fiefs of the Aymara Indians, who live in various mountain and altiplano areas between Lake Titicaca and Lake Poopó.

Bol/146 and Bol/147. *Subdesert Puna on the Bolivian altiplano and course of the Desaguadero river.* Pages 218 and 220.

One notes human settlement by the eucalyptus woods, near the curve of the railway, which suddenly swerves from its formerly straight course southwards to Oruro. In the south-eastern part of the picture, amidst the lakes, a tin mine bares its white erosion scar.

Bol/148. *Tropical rain forest in north-eastern Bolivia, course of the Maniquí river and town of San Borja.* Page 45.

In this largely uninhabited region, activity focuses nowadays around timber and oil. A manifestation of the latter industry shows with the path of the pipeline reaching Trinidad. Lost in the jungles and swamplands, a few roads manage to appear, as minute white streaks amidst the red immensity, which connect the few settlers with "civilization".

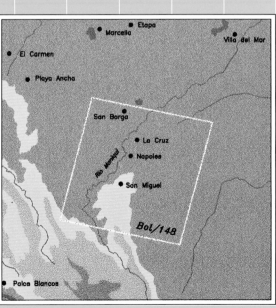

Map 52

197

2°30'

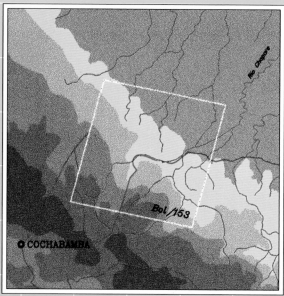

Map 53

Bol/149

Bol/150.

3°

3°30'

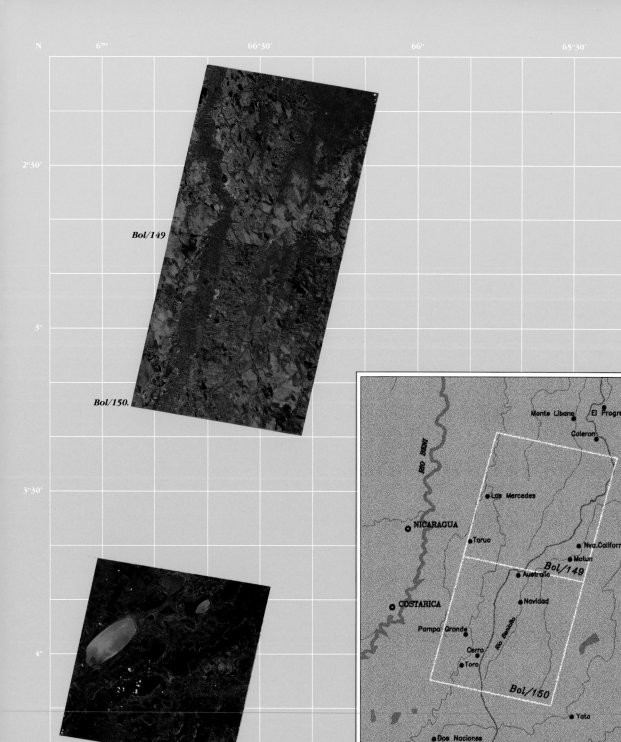

Bol/151. Pg. 18.

4°

Bol/149 and Bol/150. *Uninhabited zone of north-eastern Bolivia's tropical rain forest.*

This zone combines jungle, river and swamp, where no human activity is found. To the east, one detects functional radiometric anomalies in the satellite's sensors. In the picture, one observes the straight line of the north-south road towards the cordilleras.

4°30'

5°

Map 54

Map 55

Bol/151. *Cluster of small lakes originating from the rivers and swamps close to north-eastern Bolivia's tropical rain forest.* **Page 18.**

The small, shallow lakes of Rogagua, Yusala, La Nieve, and Santa Clara, to mention but a few, represent the zone's water reserves. The village of La Nieve lies on a strategic road leading to the Brazilian border.

Bol/153. Pg. 227.

Bol/152. *Llanos de Mojos and course of the Río Grande on the humid savannah in eastern Bolivia.*

Recent settlement is channelled through the Río Grande, which flows across the picture towards Paraguay. One notes that settlement grows along the road. Fields, showing in red strips, are planted with rice or cassava. To the north-eastern part of the picture, one can discern a star-shaped area of cultivation, spreading from a human settlement. Besides "official" settlements, one observes other, more clandestine, deforestation focal points, dedicated to lumbering. In these territories, destitute immigrants from the cordillera find no other way to survive than clearing the jungle and cultivating the meager subsoil.

Bol/153. *Transition zone between Bolivia's eastern Cordillera, near Cochabamba, and the region of Chaparé.* **Page 227.**

This zone, eminently suitable for agriculture, gathers over a million people. Still organized along the same pattern as in the days of the Inca, farmlands are small, an average of less than two hectares, and irrigated by rivers and streams flowing down from the cordillera. Rice, bananas and citrus fruits are the main crops.

Bol/154. *Tributaries of the Piray and Río Grande rivers in the Llanos de Mojos, on eastern Bolivia's humid savannah.*

Today, this is a Bolivian government priority settlement area in the country's eastern stretches. One notes human presence by the roads along the tributaries of the Piray and Río Grande rivers. Destitute people from the highlands, usually Indians, come to settle locally to plant rice and cassava, or work on the oilfields.

Bol/155. *City of Gran Santa Cruz de la Sierra, on Bolivia's tropical savannah foothills.*

One observes the south-western slopes of the cordillera sweep down to the plains of Santa Cruz, and the course of the Piray river and its tributaries. The city of Gran Santa Cruz de la Sierra, commonly known as Santa Cruz, with its star shape and concentric growth circles, represents the latest episode in Bolivia's boom cycle after silver and tin: oil. Santa Cruz, the country's tropical metropolis, has a population of 700,000 people, with two airports, the old one downtown and the new, international Viru-Viru to the north. Other oil boomtowns close-by, like Warmes, play the role of bridgeheads for the colonization of the plains further north.

Bol/156. *Santa Cruz, Bolivia's oil capital.*

The city of Santa Cruz, which mushroomed in the fifties from forgotten, dusty boondocks to affluence when oil was struck, now acts as a gateway to Brazil and Argentina. It pertains to an extremely humid climatic zone, which turns dry to the south and east. The Piray river is the city's water supply. Timber barons exploit the nearby forests, and meat-packing industries thrive thanks to bountiful local cattle.

Bol/152.

Bol/154.

Bol/155.

Bol/156.

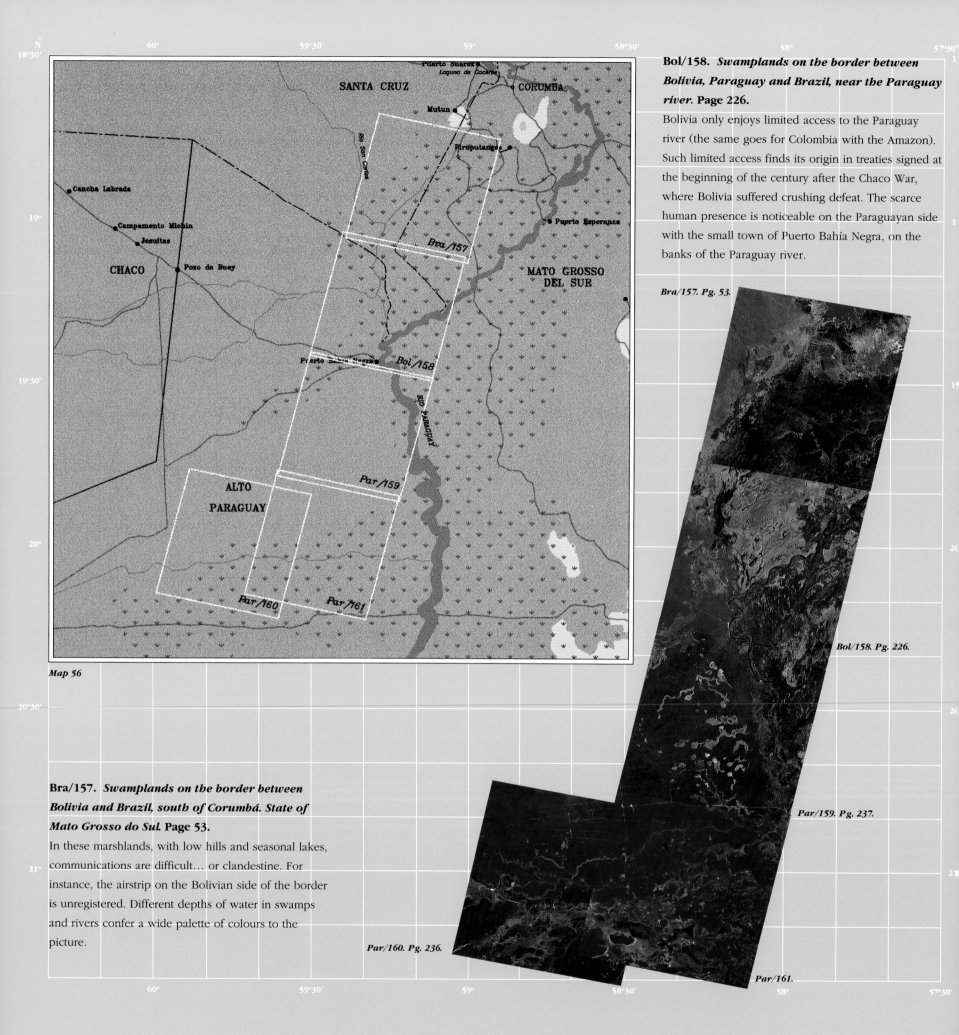

Bol/158. *Swamplands on the border between Bolivia, Paraguay and Brazil, near the Paraguay river.* **Page 226.**

Bolivia only enjoys limited access to the Paraguay river (the same goes for Colombia with the Amazon). Such limited access finds its origin in treaties signed at the beginning of the century after the Chaco War, where Bolivia suffered crushing defeat. The scarce human presence is noticeable on the Paraguayan side with the small town of Puerto Bahía Negra, on the banks of the Paraguay river.

Bra/157. Pg. 53.

Bol/158. Pg. 226.

Par/159. Pg. 237.

Map 56

Bra/157. *Swamplands on the border between Bolivia and Brazil, south of Corumbá. State of Mato Grosso do Sul.* **Page 53.**

In these marshlands, with low hills and seasonal lakes, communications are difficult… or clandestine. For instance, the airstrip on the Bolivian side of the border is unregistered. Different depths of water in swamps and rivers confer a wide palette of colours to the picture.

Par/160. Pg. 236.

Par/161.

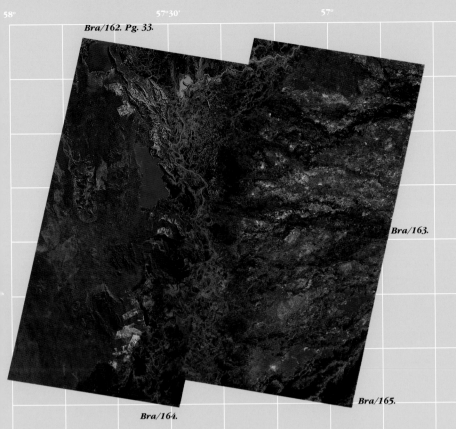

Bra/162. Pg. 33.

Bra/163.

Bra/164.

Bra/165.

18°

18°30'

19°

19°30'

20°

20°30'

Par/161. *The Paraguay river in the tropical savannah swamplands between Paraguay and Brazil.*

The zone is highly subject to floods, because of wild fluctuations in river volume, which explains the eccentric effects of water erosion on the landscape. Presence of shallow waters is revealed by dark patches and sinuous squiggles in the hydrographic system.

Bra/162. *Border between Bolivia and Brazil, west and east of the lakes, a hundred kilometres north of the town of Corumbá.* **Page 33.**

The biggest lake, at the centre of the picture, is the Mandioré, split in two by the frontier line. The lake to the north is La Gaiba, also shared between the two countries. On the Bolivian side, one notes an agricultural settlement; on the Brazilian side, the course of the Lourenço river.

Par/159. *Border zone between Paraguay and Brazil west and east of the Paraguay river.* **Page 237.**

The course of the Paraguay river divides not only two nations but also two distinct geographical zones. In Paraguay, west of the river, tropical savannahs merge into the subdesert Chaco. In Brazil, vast swamplands, with hill ranges of difficult access, blend into the Mato Grosso. Only Paraguay asserts its presence locally, with a road system.

Par/160. *Marshy tropical savannah of Paraguay, near the Paraguay river on the border with Brazil.* **Page 236.**

The zone is highly subject to floods, because of wild fluctuations in river volume, which explains the eccentric effects of water erosion on the landscape. In this recently-settled zone, of uncertain economic promise until the existence of local oilfields is confirmed, human presence is explained by strategic rather than economic interests.

Bra/163. *Course of the Lourenço river, a tributary of the Paraguay, in Brazil near the border with Bolivia.*

The Lourenço's swampy nature is revealed by overwhelming red in the picture, a red which turns deeper as the river nears the Paraguay. To the east, the scars of human industry stand out in white: roads, extensive cultivations, cattle fields…

Bra/164. *Course of the Paraguay river on the border between Brazil and Bolivia, north of Corumbá.*

The picture is divided into two geographical zones: swamplands in Brazilian territory, where the meanders of the Paraguay river sustain aquatic vegetation, appearing in red; and Bahía Vermelha, to the north, in black.

Bra/165. *Small town of Santa Cruz, in the swamplands of the remote Brazilian interior near the Bolivian border.*

This is a swampland which receives tributaries of the Paraguay river. In the picture, one sees the small, scattered town of Santa Cruz (unrelated to its Bolivian namesake), with a road passing through swamps and rivers.

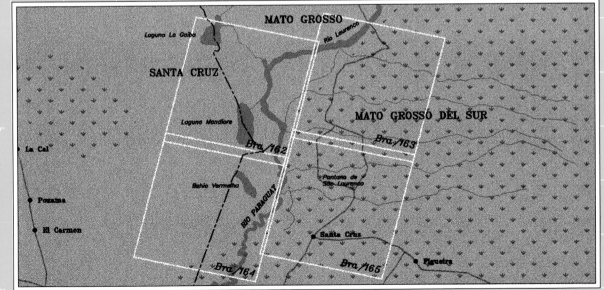

MATO GROSSO

Laguna La Gaiba

Rio Lourenço

SANTA CRUZ

MATO GROSSO DEL SUR

Laguna Mandiore

Bra/162

Bra/163

La Cal

Bahía Vermelha

Pontone de São-Lourenço

RIO PARAGUAY

Pozaina

El Carmen

Santa Cruz

Bra/164

Bra/165

Figueira

Map 57

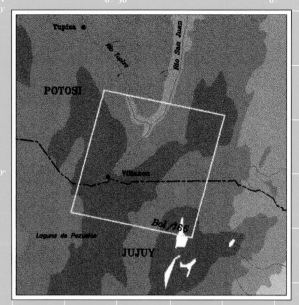

Map 58

Bol/166. *Small town of Villazón in the semi-arid southern stretches of the Bolivian altiplano, on the border with Argentina.* Page 8.

The town is located exactly on the frontier with Argentina and at the source of the San Juan river, the course of which slices northwards through the altiplano, leaving a deep scar. A road on the Bolivian side goes from south to north. In this desert of rock and sand, one detects a few signs of vegetation in the ravine carved by the San Juan river.

Bol/167. *Immense slopes of the Bolivian Cordillera sweeping down to the Chaco oil plains.* Page 224.

One observes human presence outside the desert mountain slopes, the canyons of which channel the rivers springing above into a north-south direction. On the plains one notes roads and pipelines leading to the north-western populated regions.

Bol/168. *Transition zone between the vast slopes of the Cordillera and the Chaco plains.* Page 222.

The small villages along the rectilinear roads are recent, and belong to a wave of colonization coming from the Chaco plains, with its rich oil and gas deposits. This zone is of strategic importance for its energy resources and proximity to the border with Paraguay.

Bol/169. *Flat stretches of the Bolivian Chaco in the transition zone between dry tropical jungle and savannah.* Page 223.

The north of the picture show traces of surface water through layer infiltration typical of the plains. The activity of this recently settled zone centres on petroleum: gas is exported to Paraguay and oil reserved for national consumption.

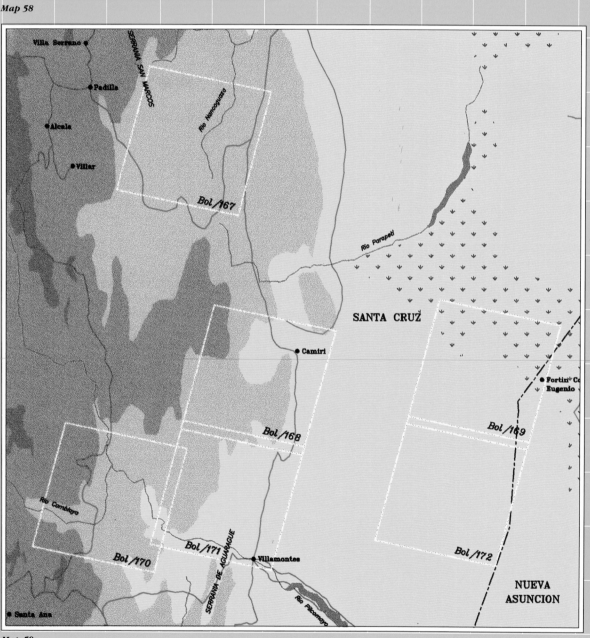

Map 59

Bol/166. Pg. 8.

Bol/167. Pg. 224.

Bol/172. *Dry tropical shrublands of the Chaco, near the border with Paraguay.*

Colonization is organized in this region, of strategic importance for its closeness to the border, as shown by the rectilinear path of roads dividing small farmholdings. Settlements are scattered over an immense territory. Activities focus on extensive cattle raising (meat is either consumed in the highlands or exported to Paraguay) and oil and gas prospecting.

Bol/170. *Vast slopes of the Bolivian Cordillera Real's eastern foothills, preceding the Chaco shrublands.* Page 37.

These vast slopes are almost completely barren, with parallel north-south rocky ranges. One observes the dried-out riverbeds extending along the ranges, before flowing down eastwards to the Chaco plains. The only resources of this isolated zone are reserves of gas and oil, which are exported directly to Argentina and Brazil.

Bol/170. Pg. 37.

Bol/168. Pg. 222.

Bol/169. Pg. 223.

Bol/172.

Bol/171. Pg. 219.

Bol/171. *Small town of Villa Montes in the transition zone between the slopes of the Bolivian Cordillera and the Chaco plains.* Page 219.

The Pilcomayo river, the source of which lies high up in the cordillera, flows into Paraguay after passing through most of the cordillera and Chaco. The slopes, dry and unproductive, constitute a transition zone preceding the savannah, where the main town is Villa Montes, which lies on the Pilcomayo, on the pipeline and the communication route southwards to Argentina and eastwards to Paraguay. The town's activities stem mainly from the oil industry. Roads running parallel to the cordillera lead to La Paz and Santa Cruz, Bolivia's two economic capitals. Over the slopes, one notes high-altitude oval cloud formations showing in blue.

Chi/173. *Salt deserts in the altiplanos of northern Chile, on the border zone with Bolivia.* Page 228.

In this region, rich in copper and nitrates, with a hallucinatory lunar scenery, brimming with signs of volcanic activity, craters, lava flows and ash, human presence is strictly limited to a few battered roads where vehicles only pass once in a blue moon. The big white patch to the north corresponds to the Salar de Coipasa, the salt crystal surface of which intensely reflects sunlight.

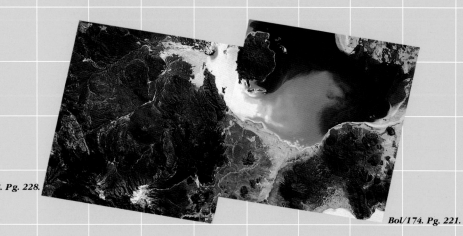

Chi/173. Pg. 228.

Bol/174. Pg. 221.

Bol/174. *Salar de Coipasa in the desert stretches of Bolivia's south-western altiplano.* Page 221.

This extremely desolate zone is totally devoid of water. The salt desert was formed by the drying up of thawing snows saturated with salt from mountain surface rock. One notes the little depth of the salt layer by the pale colours. Of course, in such a salty environment, no vegetation grows. A similar, vastly larger desert, the Uyuni, lies to the south-east.

Chi/175. *Deserts of northern Chile's altiplano, near the frontier with Bolivia.* Page 229.

At over 4,000 m. above sea level, this region lies on the northern expanses of the Acatama desert, rich in copper, gold and nitrate deposits. The picture shows the colours of volcanic rock, sand, ash and salt; not a speck of the red characteristic of vegetation. The scarcity of water is denoted by the dried-up, rugged beds of seasonal rivers and streams.

Chi/175. Pg. 229.

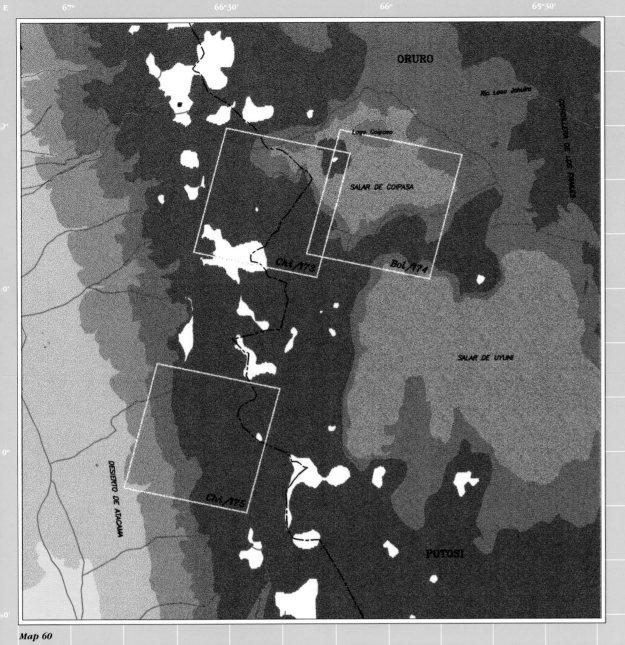

ORURO

CORDILLERA DE LOS FRAILES

Río Lacca Jahuira

Loma Colpana

SALAR DE COIPASA

Cht./173

Bol./174

SALAR DE UYUNI

DESIERTO DE ATACAMA

Cht./175

POTOSI

Map 60

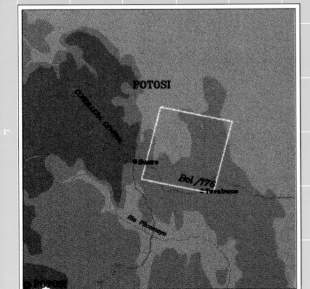

POTOSI

CORDILLERA CENTRAL

Sucre

Bol./176

Tarabuco

Río Pilcomayo

POTOSI

Map 61

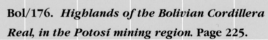

Bol/176. Pg. 225.

Bol/176. *Highlands of the Bolivian Cordillera Real, in the Potosí mining region.* Page 225.

During the period of *La Conquista*, the Potosí silver mines generated colossal wealth for the Spanish Crown, and an extensive network of communication routes with Lima. Later, tin came to supplant depleted silver. Unfortunately, mining profits were not reinvested in the region. In these awe-inspiring mountains, exclusively dependent on mining, the 1986 dramatic drop of tin prices had disastrous effects. In the southern part of the picture, the city of Sucre to the west and village of Tarabuco to the east went through all the cycles of mining booms, silver and tin. Human presence in this remarkable area of the cordillera dates back to the dawn of time, and can be detected in ancient settlements at impossible altitudes over vertiginous canyons.

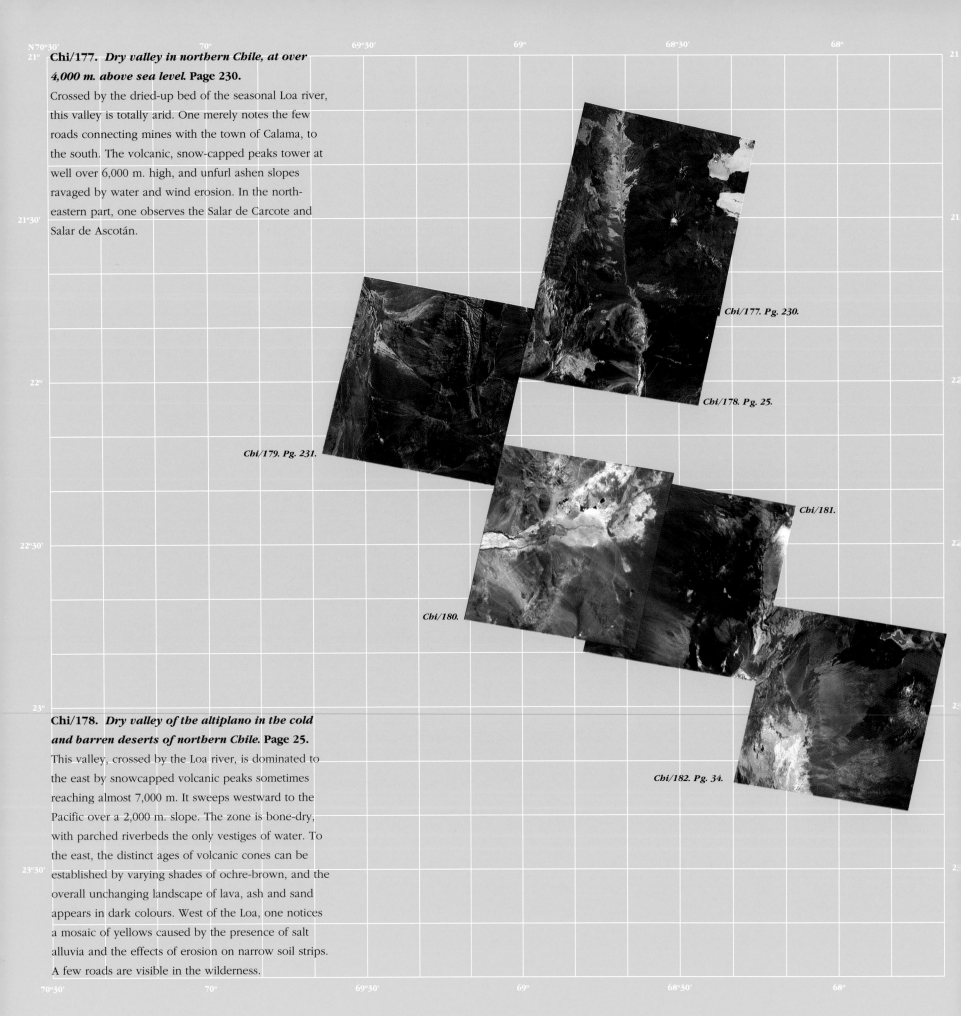

Chi/177. *Dry valley in northern Chile, at over 4,000 m. above sea level.* **Page 230.**

Crossed by the dried-up bed of the seasonal Loa river, this valley is totally arid. One merely notes the few roads connecting mines with the town of Calama, to the south. The volcanic, snow-capped peaks tower at well over 6,000 m. high, and unfurl ashen slopes ravaged by water and wind erosion. In the north-eastern part, one observes the Salar de Carcote and Salar de Ascotán.

Chi/177. Pg. 230.

Chi/178. Pg. 25.

Chi/179. Pg. 231.

Chi/181.

Chi/180.

Chi/182. Pg. 34.

Chi/178. *Dry valley of the altiplano in the cold and barren deserts of northern Chile.* **Page 25.**

This valley, crossed by the Loa river, is dominated to the east by snowcapped volcanic peaks sometimes reaching almost 7,000 m. It sweeps westward to the Pacific over a 2,000 m. slope. The zone is bone-dry, with parched riverbeds the only vestiges of water. To the east, the distinct ages of volcanic cones can be established by varying shades of ochre-brown, and the overall unchanging landscape of lava, ash and sand appears in dark colours. West of the Loa, one notices a mosaic of yellows caused by the presence of salt alluvia and the effects of erosion on narrow soil strips. A few roads are visible in the wilderness.

Chi/179. *Vast slopes in northern Chile's desert zones, near the harbour of Tocopilla.* **Page 231.**

The zone is composed of ash and sand, with mineral ore and nitrate deposits. The course of the road, built to carry out minerals, runs perpendicular to slopes and parallel to valleys. There's no trace of vegetation throughout the entire zone.

Chi/180. *Northern Chile's desert, with the town of Calama on the Loa river, and the Chuquicamata copper mine.*

The town of Calama uses the Loa to irrigate an "oasis" agriculture of subsistence and apples and grapes for export. Furthermore, mineral ore and coal deposits provide fuel for a large thermoelectric plant. North of the town, one observes the Chuquicamata opencast copper mine, the world's largest (Chile also happens to be the world's major copper producer). And the Atacama region yields iron and manganese. This high-altitude valley is closed to the south by the Limón Verde hills over Calama, at 1,000 m. above sea level. There's hardly any difference between the three pictures because of the total absence of rain and snow.

Chi/181. *Mining areas around the town of Calama in Chile's eastern Cordillera.*

The picture of this zone, east of the previous Chi/180, displays the eastern slope of the mineral ore-rich cordillera. (copper, iron, nitrates, manganese and gold). There's not a drop of water in the bleak landscape, and human activities are mainly concentrated in the town of Calama. On the eastern edge of the cordillera, one finds the traditional town of San Pedro de Atacama, verging on the Salar de Atacama wastes.

Chi/182. *Salar de Atacama and town of San Pedro de Atacama, on the San Pedro river.* **Page 34.**

The town of San Pedro de Atacama, to the south of the picture, situated on the estuary of the San Pedro and at the junction of several roads, delimits the northern shore of the Salar de Atacama, at an average of 3,400 m. above sea level. An immense, snow-covered slope plunges downwards. The town of Toconoa, to the east, is a stopover towards northern hinterlands. To the north-east of the picture, one sees Laguna Verde, saturated with minerals and salt, but showing in blue nonetheless.

Map 62

207

Arg/183. *Desert aspect of north-western Argentina on the border with Chile. Province of Jujuy.* Page 233.

No-one lingers along the road in these high and forbidding zones of rock, sand and ash. As in Chile, the latter contain mineral ore deposits, copper, manganese and nitrates, but in lesser quantities. Minerals from these mines are traded in the foothill town of San Salvador de Jujuy. To the north of the picture, one observes Salina Grande, where several seasonal rivers flow, and also small salt and snow water lakes, at over 5,000 m. above sea level.

Arg/184. *Mining altiplano in the desert zone of north-western Argentina. Province of Salta.* Page 234.

Human presence is limited to the immediate vicinity of roads and mining areas. The zone's volcanic and barren nature, with its craters, ash, rock and sand, reflects in local geographic names: the Sierra de Aguas Calientes mountain range crossing the picture, and the Salar del Hombre Muerto salt desert to the south-east. By the side of the road, one observes the Tingalayu airstrip, used to ship out mineral production.

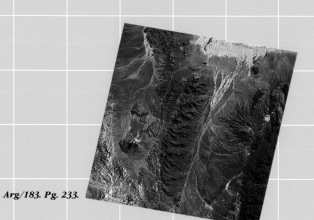

Arg/183. Pg. 233.

Arg/184. Pg. 234.

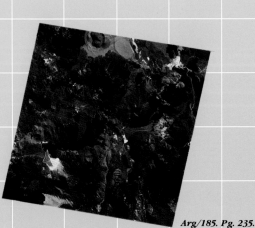

Arg/185. Pg. 235.

Arg/186. Pg. 21.

Arg/185. *Desert zone of the mining altiplano along the northern frontier between Chile and Argentina. Province of Salta.* Page 235.

Mountain peaks of over 6,000 m. soar over these barren volcanic wastelands. Lakes, which show as blue droplets in the picture, are fed by the snow thawing from high-altitude mountains. White patches reveal volcanic activity and an environment abounding in salt and sulphur.

Arg/186. *Salar del Hombre Muerto along the Sierra de Aguas Calientes. Province of Salta, Argentina.* Page 21.

The pinkish-grey colour is characteristic of a totally waterless salt desert, blue of saltwater, white of accumulated dry salt strata. Mountain peaks soar to more than 5,000 m. Towns, roads and the railway lie 200 km. further eastward, at the foot of the altiplano.

Arg/187.

Arg/188. Pg. 232.

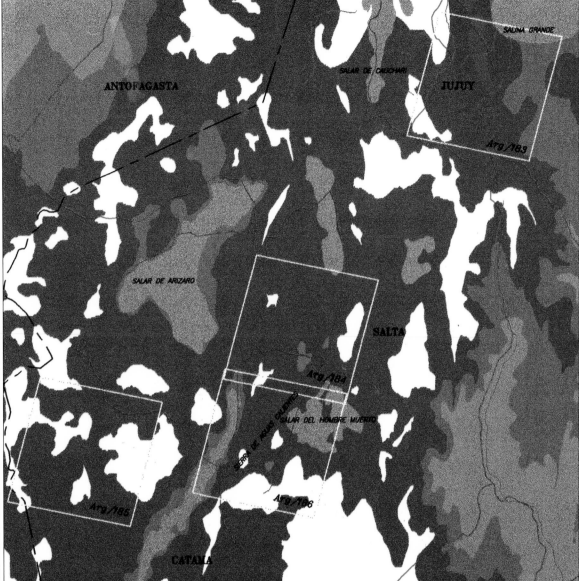

Arg/187. _Parallel courses of the Río Seco and Río Bermejo rivers along the jungle hills north-west of Argentina and south of Bolivia._

In this foothill zone, a highly-organized agro-industry shows in the neat, regular pattern of fields, from the towns of Tartagal to the north-east and Bermejo to the south-west. Profusely irrigated, these lands grow sugarcane, soybean and fruit. Produce is transported by truck to Jujuy and Tucumán. The contrast between farmlands and virgin mountains appears clearly in the different colours and formations.

Arg/188. _Oil-rich border zone close to the Bolivian Chaco, in north-western Argentina. Province of Jujuy._ Page 232.

The cordillera ends here, on the latitude of San Juan de la Nueva Oran, at the confluence between the Río Bermejo, which springs in Bolivia, and Río Blanco. On the opposite side of the coils of the Río Bermejo lies the small town of Embarcación, near the lake where the Río Seco flows in from the north. On these abundantly-irrigated fields, sugarcane, soybean and fruit are grown on an industrial scale.

Map 63

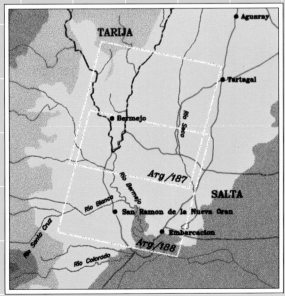

Map 64

Region of "La Chala" in south-western Peru.
Province of Arequipa.

Per/132, page 194

The Peruvian Andes south-east of Arequipa.
Province of Moquegua.

Per/133, page 194

The Cordillera in southern Peru
near the border with Chile, in the province of Tacna.

Per/135, page 195

Peruvian border zone,
north of Chile and west of Bolivia.

Per/136, page 195

Eastern foothills of the Bolivian Cordillera,
the colossal Illampú and the town of Caranavi.

Bol/137, page 196

*Dry altiplano and snowcapped mountain range
in the central area of Bolivia's Cordillera Real.*

Bol/143, page 196

Snowcapped peaks of the Illimani,
which tower over La Paz, the Bolivian administrative capital.

Bol/138, page 196

The Cordillera Real and the dry Puna plateau
which stretches between La Paz and Oruro.

Bol/142, page 196

*Sub-desert Puna on the Bolivian altiplano
and course of the Desaguadero river.*

Bol/146, page 196

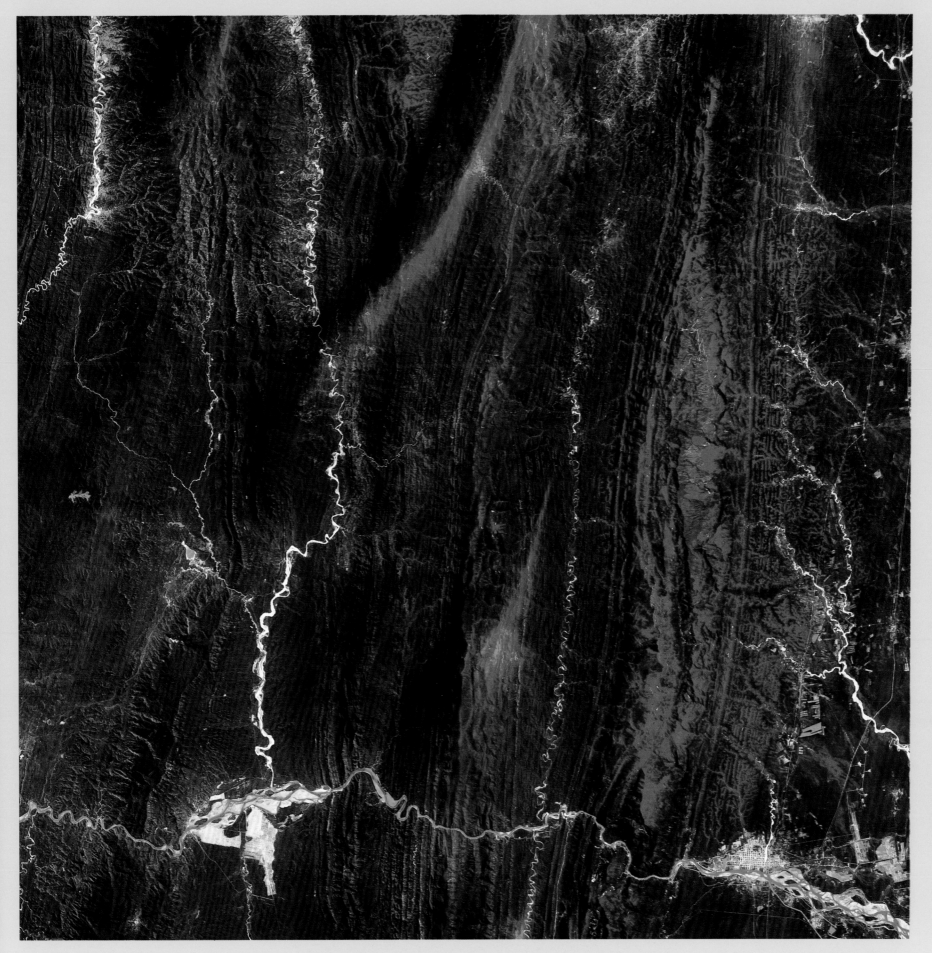

*Small town of Villa Montes in the transition zone between the
slopes of the Bolivian Cordillera and the Chaco plains.*

Bol/171, page 203

*Sub-desert Puna on the Bolivian altiplano
and course of the Desaguadero river.*

Bol/147, page 196

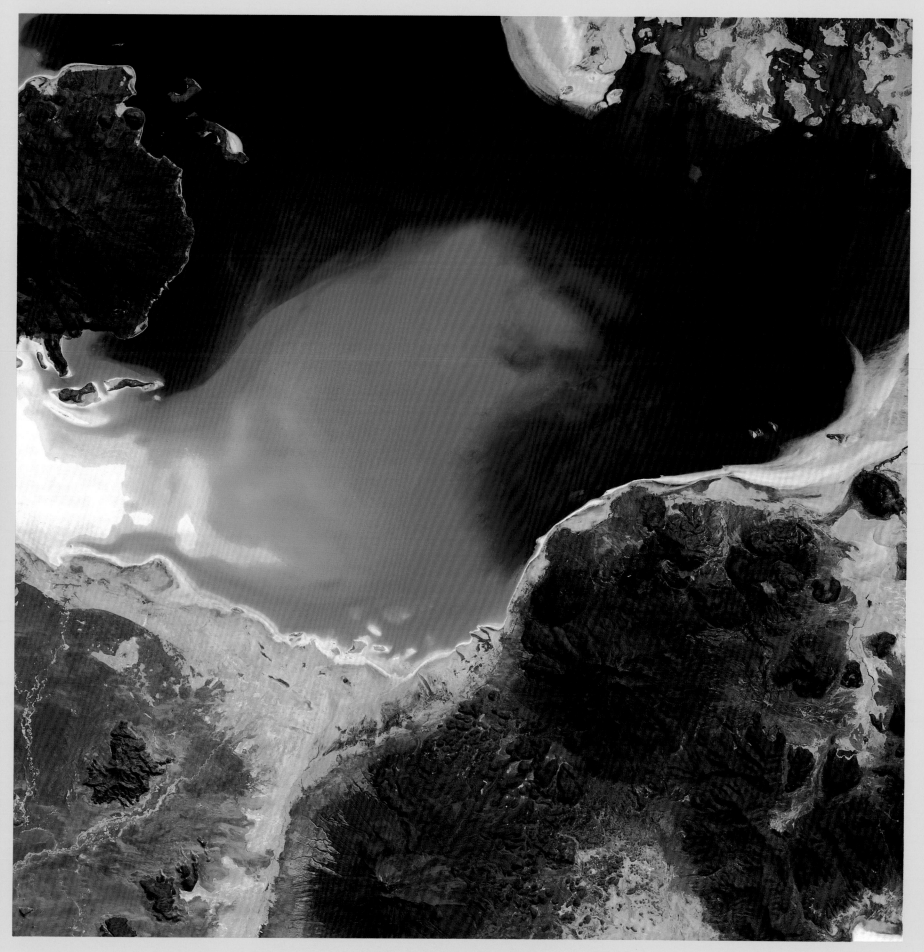

*Salar de Coipasa in the desert stretches
of Bolivia's south-western altiplano.*

Bol/174, page 204

*Transition zone between the vast slopes
of the Cordillera and the Chaco plains.*

Bol/168, page 203

Flat stretches of the Bolivian Chaco in the transition zone
between dry tropical jungle and savannah.

Bol/169, page 203

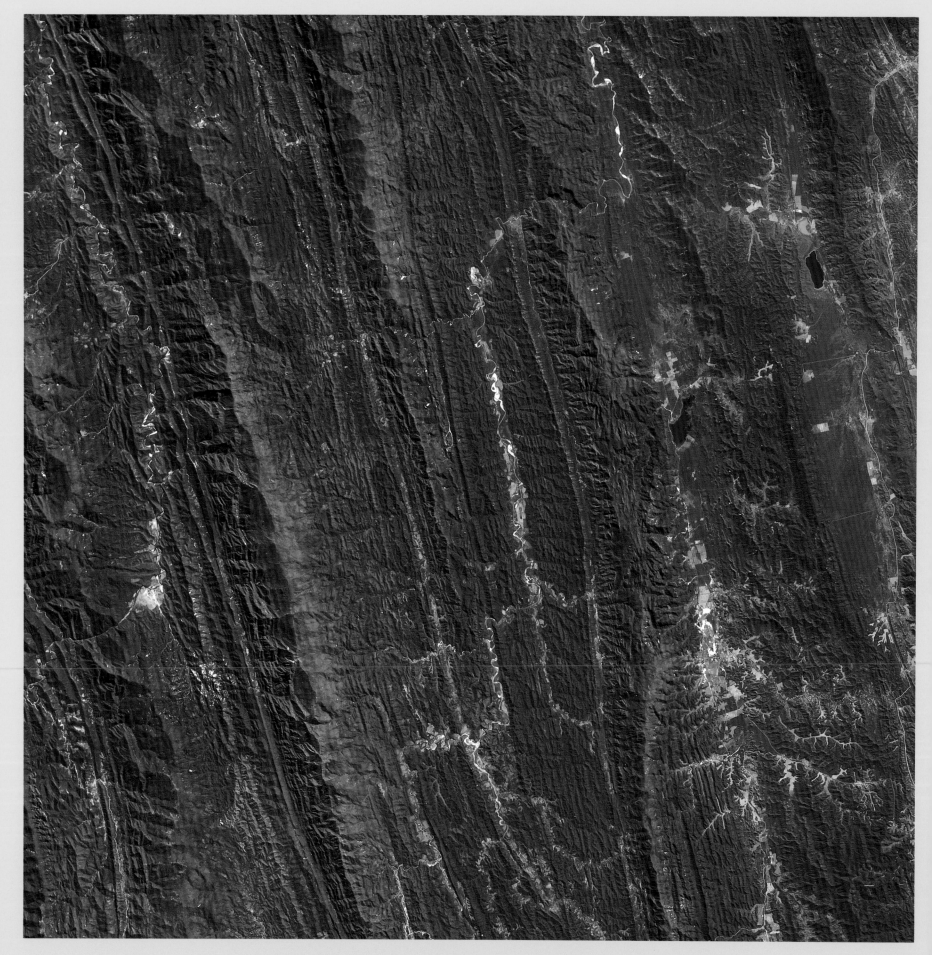

Salt deserts in the altiplanos of northern Chile,
on the border zone with Bolivia.

Chi/173, page 204

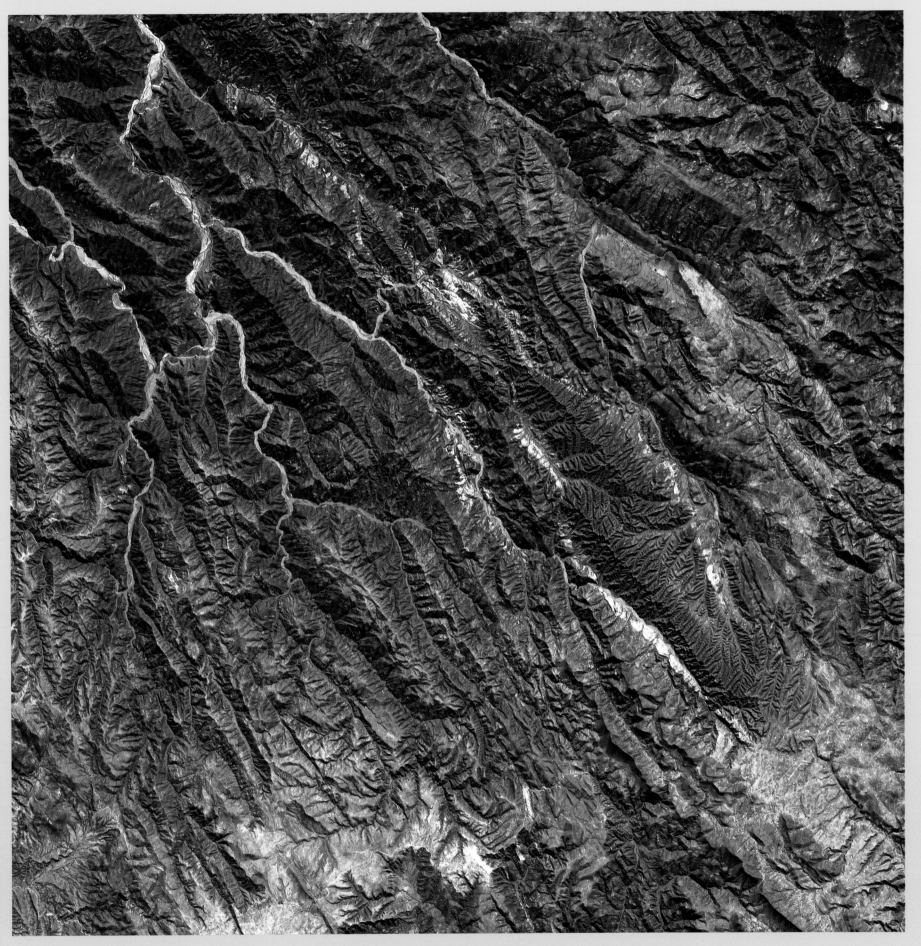

*Highlands of the Bolivian Cordillera Real
in the Potosí mining region.*

Bol/176, page 205

Swamplands on the border between Bolivia,
Paraguay and Brazil, near the Paraguay river.

Bol/158, page 200

Transition zone between Bolivia's eastern Cordillera,
near Cochabamba, and the region of Chaparé.

Bol/153, page 199

Immense slopes of the Bolivian Cordillera
sweeping down to the Chaco oil plains.

Bol/167, page 203

Deserts of northern Chile's altiplano,
near the frontier with Bolivia.

Chi/175, page 204

Dry valley in northern Chile,
at over 4,000 m. above sea level.

Chi/177, page 206

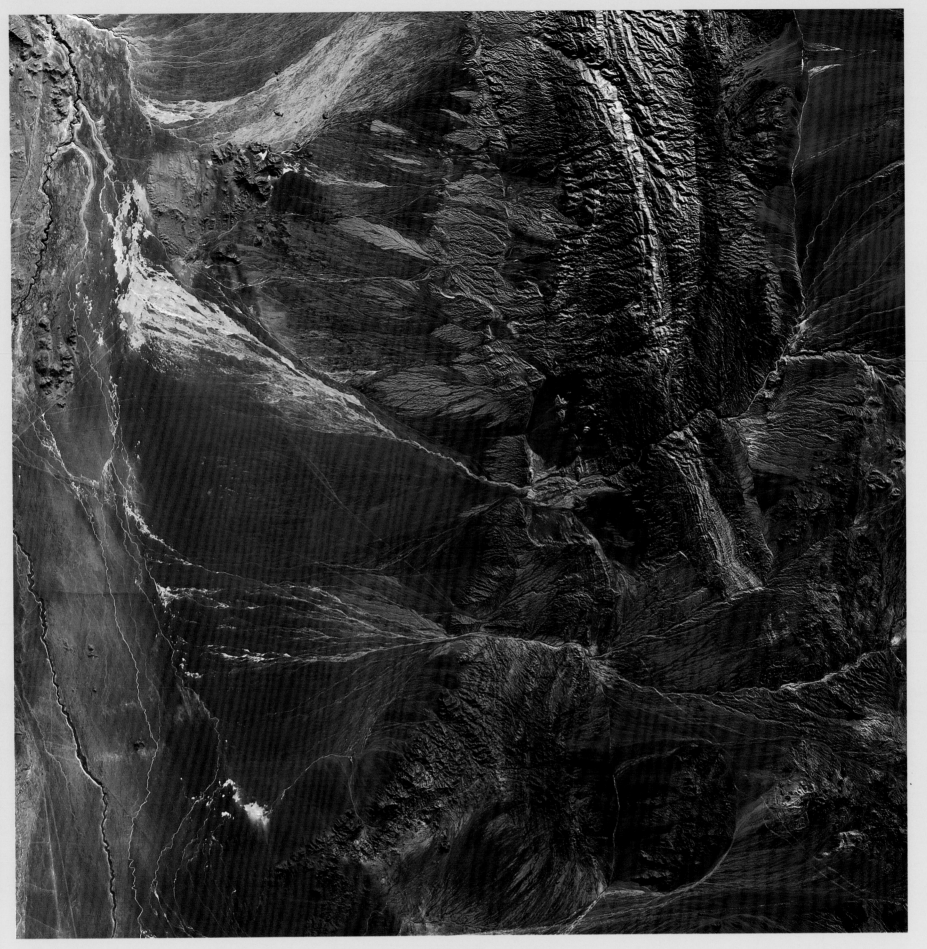

*Vast slopes in northern Chile's desert zones,
near the harbour of Tocopilla.*

Chi/179, page 206

Oil-rich border zone close to the Bolivian Chaco,
in north-western Argentina. Province of Jujuy.

Arg/188, page 209

Desert aspect of north-western Argentina
on the border with Chile. Province of Jujuy.

Arg/183, page 208

*Mining altiplano in the desert zone
of north-western Argentina. Province of Salta.*

Arg/184, page 208

*Desert zone of the mining altiplano along the northern
frontier between Chile and Argentina. Province of Salta.*

Arg/185, page 208

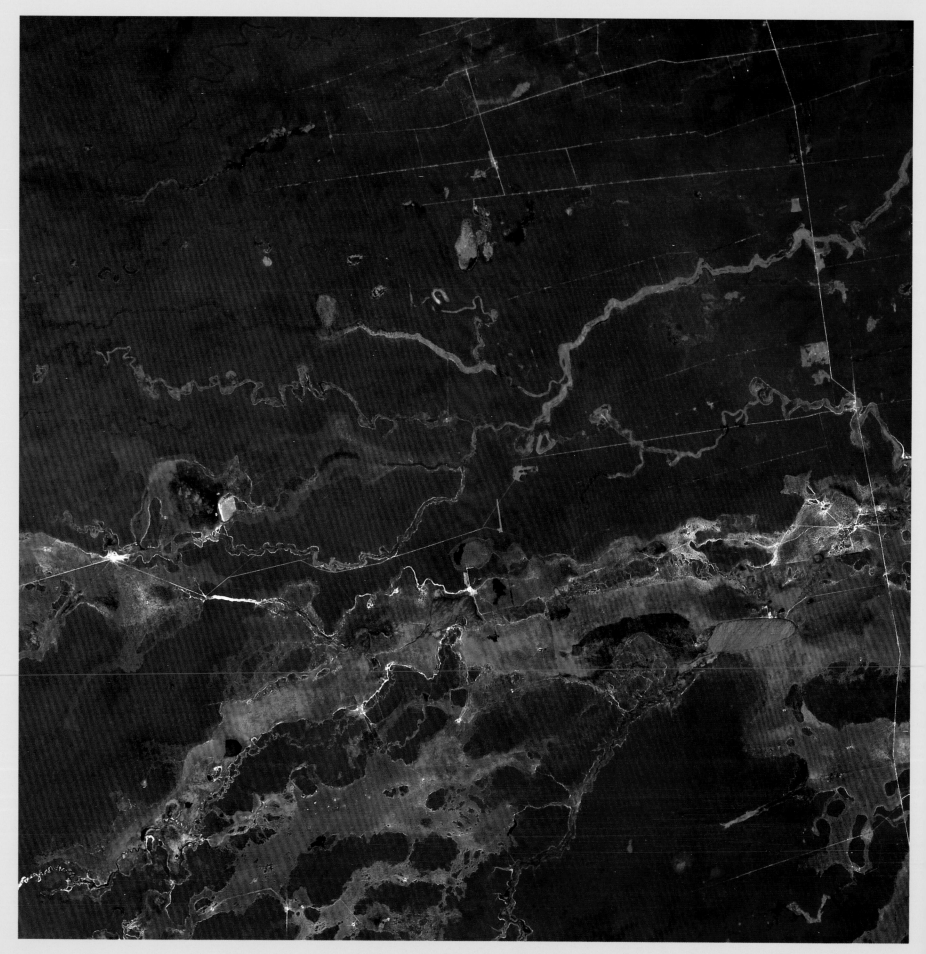

Marshy tropical savannah of Paraguay,
near the Paraguay river on the border with Brazil.

Par/160, page 200

Index

Nomenclature or color interpretation

 Blue: Sea or continental shallow waters.

 Yellow: Sand, rocks and bare land.

 White: Superficial clouds, sand, rocks, snow, salt, saltwaters.

 Gray: Cities.

 Brown and ocher: Agricultural activity, sand, minor bare land, rock desserts, ashes.

 Black: Sea or continental waters, rivers and lakes.

 Red: Vegetation, the red is more intense as clorophile activity increases.

 Green: Agricultural activity, country side, plantations and pastures.

Example: Pages 84, 85 and 115.

Technical Bibliography

AIMEDIEU, P. "La querelle de l'ozone". *La Recherche*, No. 196, février 1988, vol. 19, pp. 270-282.

BERNARD, C. Les images SPOT, outil de décision en matière de défense. *Nouvelles de SPOT*, décembre 1989, No. 12, pp. 20-21, SPOT IMAGE éd.

CNES -Ecole d'été internationale de physique spatiale- *Télédétection spatiale: aspects physiques et modélisation*. Toulouse, aout 1988, 1.032 p. Cepadues-Editions.

COLWELL, R. N. "Potential Uses of Satellite Photography for Natural Ressources Survey". *Intern. Archives of Photogram.* Vol. XV, Part. 7, pp. 33-48. Xth. Intern. Congress of Photogrammetry, Lisbonne, sept. 1964.

DEPECKER, L. *Cinq notions de télédétection aérospatiale: un exemple de structuration d'un champ terminologique*. META, XXXIV, 2, 1989, pp. 280-284.

DUCROCQ, A. "La Terre vue de l'espace". *Sciences et Avenir*, No. 227, janv. 1966, pp. 34-39.

Earth photographs from Gemini III, IV et V. Scientific and Technical Information Division. Office of Technology Utilization, NASA SP-129; Washington, DC, 266 p., 1967.

FUSSEL, J. RUNDQUIST, D. and HARRINGTON, J. A. "On Defining Remote Sensing". *Photogrammetric Engineering and Remote Sensing*, vol. 52 No. 9 sept. 1986, pp. 1507-1511.

PAUL, S. "La télédétection électromagnétique aérienne en terrains éruptifs". *La Recherche Spatiale*, No. 5, vol. XII, pp. 14-16, pl. III. Editions CNES-DUNOD París, 1973.

PAUL, S. "Terminologie de la télédétection" (dictionnaire bilingue français/anglais). *Actes des Journées de télédétection du G.D.T.A.* Toulouse, oct. 1976, t. l., pp. 51-53.

POUQUET, J. *Les sciences de la Terre à l'heure des satellites*. Presses Universitaires de France, collection SUP *Le physicien*, 260 p., 1971.

Spaceflight, série américaine écrite et présentée par Blaise BAGGETT pour la T.V. Commentée par Marten SHEEN. Globe Trotter Network, copyright 1985. Adaptation française *La Conquete de l'espace* sous la responsabilité de N. ROY, FR3, 1988.

VINOGRADOV, B. V. *Emploi des méthodes aériennes pour l'étude des eaux souterraines* (en russe). Akademiia Nauk S.S.S.R., Moskva, Léningrad, 1962.

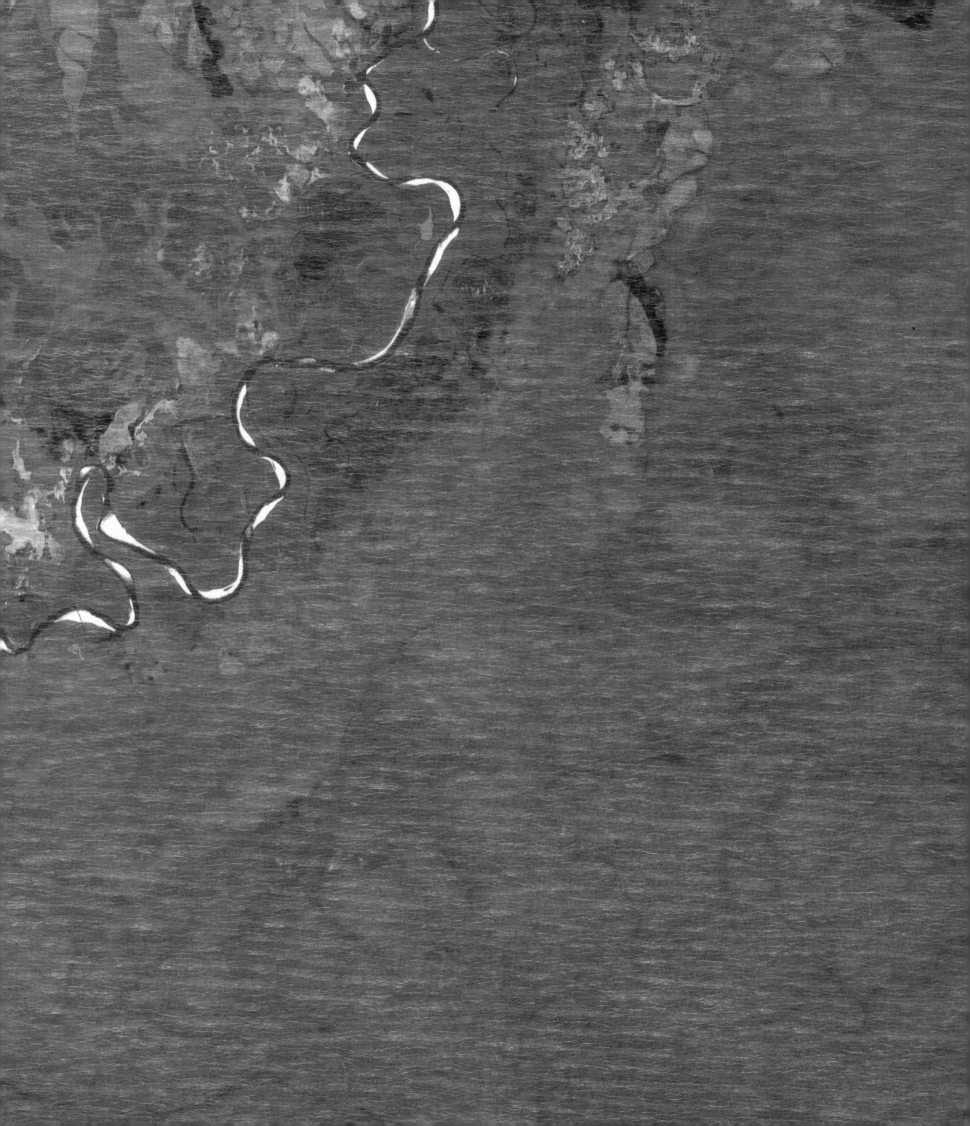

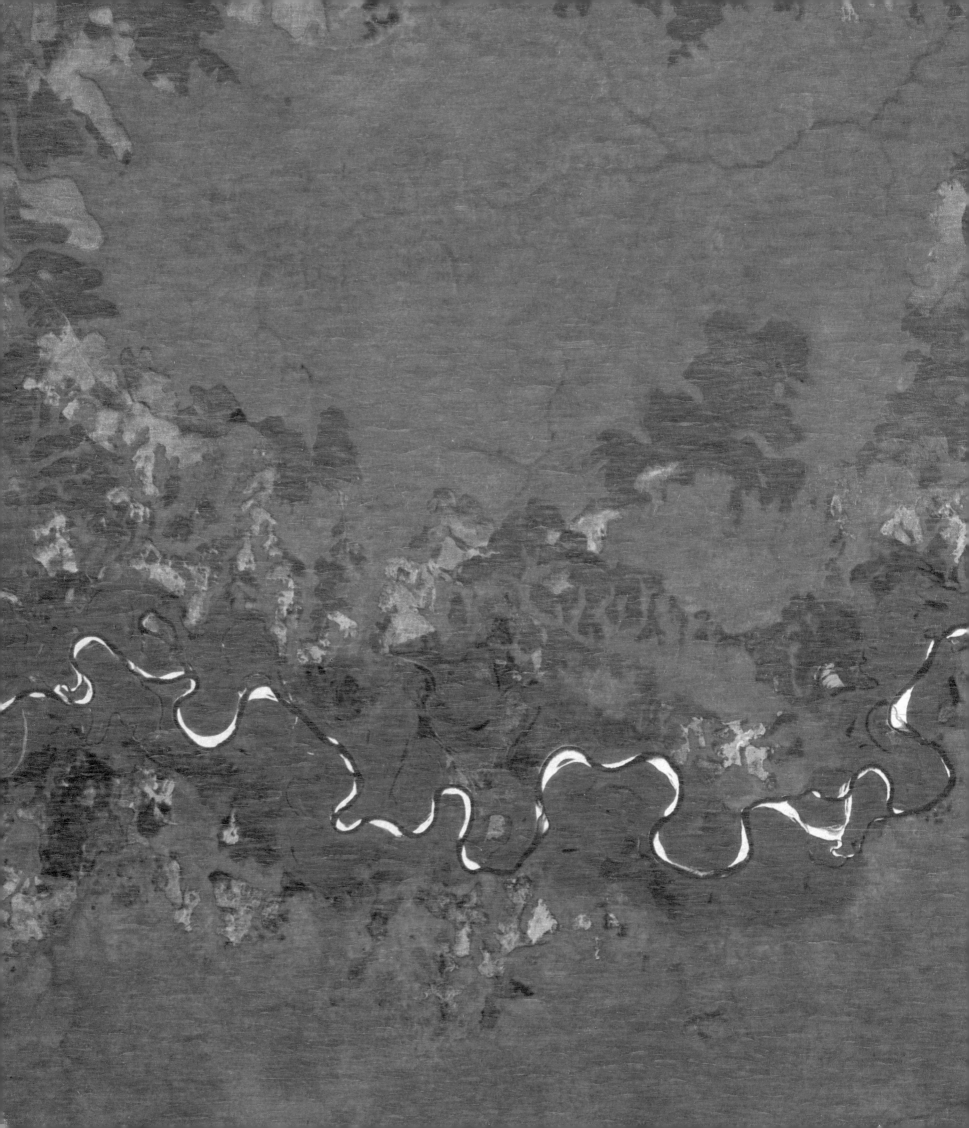